Stop Drinking 4 Life

E A S I L Y !

THERE IS NO SUCH THING AS AN ALCOHOLIC!

Jason Vale

Best selling author of *Slim 4 Life*
and *The Juice Master's Ultimate Fast Food*

JUICE MASTER PUBLICATIONS

Published by Juice Master Publications
Part of The Juice Master Ltd
22 Moseley Gate, Moseley
Birmingham, B13 8JJ

The website address is: www.thejuicemaster.com

First published in 1999
Reprinted 2006

1 3 5 7 9 10 8 6 4 2

Copyright © Jason Vale 2003

Jason Vale asserts the moral right to be
identified as the author of this work

ISBN 0-9547664-0-7

Printed and bound in Great Britain by
Biddles Limited, King's Lynn, Norfolk

Contents

A Book That Needs No Introduction

Enjoy your journey to certain freedom.

Jason Vale

1
There Is No Such Thing As An Alcoholic

For many people reading the first page of this book, the statement 'there is no such thing as an alcoholic' may seem difficult to believe and accept, particularly if you have personally been labelled with the title '*alcoholic*'. However, I intend to prove to you, without any doubt that there is no such thing as an alcoholic, as society understands it, and that there is no such disease as alcoholism.

I would like to take you on a journey to discover the truth behind the most used and accepted drug in the world. It is time for all of us to 'take our heads out of the sand' and finally face up to the truth about alcohol. Alcohol addiction has never been seen for what it really is. The subject of having a drink problem is all very 'hush hush' and the possibility of being addicted to alcohol is rarely addressed and is all too often swept under the carpet. We have been conditioned to believe that you are either a 'normal' drinker or that you have lost control and are an 'alcoholic'. So we have a situation where the people who have finally woken up to the fact that they are not in control have to keep quiet about it for fear of being made an outcast by society. If they are brave enough to voice a desire to stop drinking, they are called alcoholics suggesting that they have an incurable disease and would have to 'give up' drinking forever! This is a frightening thought for anybody who drinks.

The truth is that *nobody* is *ever* in true control of their alcohol intake, as I will prove beyond doubt in this book. In any other form of drug addiction, the addict who wants to quit is applauded by society for realising that they were never in control. With alcohol, the addict is given a label and is made to feel inferior. In reality the person who realises that they are not in control is **far** from inferior; they are well ahead of the game. After all, you can only escape from a trap when you know you are in one. The majority of people who drink alcohol have no idea that they are in any kind of trap. It is one of the subtlest traps ever devised, and has fooled millions for generations.

Alcohol has always been seen as very different from any other form of drug taking, so much so that drinking alcohol is rarely described as drug taking at all. But drug taking it is and drug addiction it is. It is the only drug in the world where, when you stop doing it, you are then seen as having a problem!

You will soon start to realise for yourself that alcohol addiction is exactly the same as any other form of drug addiction. It will soon become clear that the amount that people drink has nothing whatsoever to do with their genes, character or personality. You will soon see that the only difference between alcohol and all other drugs is the conditioning and brainwashing that we have been subjected to since birth. This book will be much more than a simple eye opener, it will change the way you see alcohol forever. This book will show you, not only how to stop drinking, should you choose to, but how you will enjoy the process and enjoy your life so much more than you do now without *having* to drink alcohol. I will also show you why nobody ever *needs* alcohol and that all the reasons for drinking is part of the most ingenious confidence trick ever to dupe mankind! They say that you can fool some of the people some of the time, but not all of the people all of the time, however, I believe that is exactly what alcohol has done. We have all been conned into believing that there are genuine benefits in taking alcohol. Many of you reading this book will be convinced that this is the case. However, I would like a chance to prove that there are no genuine benefits *whatsoever* in drinking alcohol. I do not expect you to accept or believe what I say at this stage; after all, we all have thousands of references to back up our belief that there is a good and bad side to alcohol. Nonetheless, I would like you to turn a page in your mind, open it as wide as you possibly can, so that we can begin the process of removing years of conditioning and brainwashing. It is about time we all woke up to the truth and stopped kidding ourselves. Alcohol drinking is alcohol addiction and alcohol addiction is drug addiction and drug addiction is a form of disease which gets worse and worse – unless you cure it.

Now that I have your attention please let me introduce myself. My name is Jason Vale and I am a non-drinker. Now in case you start having images of a holier than thou non-drinker whose idea of a good night out is having a cup of cocoa whilst watching lawn bowling, then you would be much mistaken. Nor am I a person who hates alcohol drinkers. I am a non-drinker but I am also a non-heroin addict and a non-crack head, but you wouldn't think any less of me for that and you certainly wouldn't pre-judge me for not taking heroin or crack. However, alcohol is seen very differently. It is the only drug where people question why you do not take it and pre-judge you if you *don't* take it!

Now to be fair, I have never been a heroin addict or a crack head, but just so that you fully understand where I am coming from, I *have* been a drinker. Well, not just a drinker, believe me, I was no slouch when it came to drinking! I was a very heavy drinker and very badly hooked (or so I thought). I was, at one stage in my life, possibly one of the world's worst *alcohol addicts* you could ever meet. Even then I knew all the reasons why I *shouldn't* drink, and at times I actually wished that I didn't need to drink, but what was my alternative? To become a non-drinker?! To be honest at the time that sounded like a disease in itself – a non-drinker! I really wouldn't have wanted to suffer with that, my life seemed bad enough as a drinker!

Even today I hate using the terms, *non-drinker* or *tee-totaller*[1] because they have such negative connotations. That is why most people pre-judge those who do not drink. I don't know about you, but when I was a drinker, whenever I heard that someone was a non-drinker, or that someone had *given up* the booze, I immediately thought boring bastard! I apologise for the language, but one of my

---

1 English term for a person who does not drink alcohol.

main fears about stopping drinking was the thought that I would turn into one of those boring bastards. I thought that if I stopped drinking I would be missing out. I thought I would feel constantly deprived of the wonderful pleasures of alcohol, the calming feeling, the relaxation, the sociable aspect of having a few beers with the lads, or a bottle of wine with dinner. The warm glow of a brandy, the crisp bite of a glass of white wine, the hot toddy, the banter, the chatter, the laughter, the merriment, the fun! In short, if I stopped drinking altogether, I thought that I would no longer have a life!

Until of course I realised that it was all nonsense.

I am pleased to say that stopping drinking certainly hasn't turned me into a bore or a social hermit, but has enhanced my social life and given me back my courage and confidence and a quality of life that I had forgotten even existed. I am now in full control of my drinking for the first time in my adult life. I now drink as much as I want to, as often as I want to and when I want to. I no longer have to exercise willpower, discipline and control not to drink too much. And every single day I have the quantity of alcohol I choose to have without having to worry about work or what people will think of me or how I am going to feel. That is true control.

The reason why I have such control now is because I do not drink alcohol any more. Not because I cannot drink it, but because I just do not want to any more. Of course I could drink alcohol whenever I wanted to, there is nothing stopping me, I simply have no desire to do so.

A few years ago I would have thought that impossible. Me, a non-drinker … never! I could not imagine what life would be like without drink. I didn't want to know what life would be like without a drink. I didn't even contemplate never drinking again. The mere thought of stopping altogether would be far too scary to even consider. Who would want to spend the rest of their lives never being allowed to drink? Not me! Whenever I started to realise that I was drinking a little too much, I would look for ways to *control* my drinking more, without having to stop completely. I would look for ways to cut down. I would look at all of the different ways that I could reduce my intake. Go 'on the wagon"[2] for a while perhaps or make every other drink a soft drink. I would drink water with alcohol to stop the dehydration or even discipline myself to not go out on certain nights to help reduce my intake, but to stop altogether, for the rest of my life? NEVER!

I once managed to 'go on the wagon' for three months. It was one of the worst of my life, I felt miserable and deprived and stayed in most of the time. I thought, what is the point of going out to a social gathering if I am not drinking? How can you possibly enjoy yourself at a social gathering without alcohol?

I now haven't touched a drop of alcohol for over three years and it has been without question, the best three years of my life. I have never once missed alcohol since I have stopped and I now socialise more now than ever before. I do not feel miserable and depressed not drinking, because there is nothing to feel miserable about. In fact I feel elated to be free from what was a constant battle to gain control. I feel so relieved to be mentally and physically free.

So just how badly addicted was I? When I was in my late teens I would get through sixteen pints of lager every day. At the weekends I would then drink even more. I used to drink Special Brew and Thunderbird, sometimes for breakfast! This went on for a couple of years. I was warned that I might be an alcoholic. I personally did not think I was. After all I was only enjoying a drink just like everybody else, only I drank a little more than most that's all! However, the more people told me I was drinking too much, the more conscious I became of it. At this stage you may agree that I was an alcoholic such is the power of social conditioning. After all, if you ever drink in the morning, you must be!

So I decided one day that enough was enough and I should reduce my intake. This should have been impossible if I were an alcoholic, after all that is the difference isn't it? Drinkers are in control, alcoholics cannot control. However, I did manage to reach the stage where I could control my drinking just like everybody else. I went from being what society would call an alcoholic to a *normal* drinker. This obviously meant that I wasn't an alcoholic after all and that I didn't

---

2 Complete abstinence from alcohol for a set period of time.

really have a problem with alcohol. After all I was now back in control and if you are in control, there is no problem. I made a point of only drinking at weekends. Oh and at birthday parties. Oh yes and at weddings and restaurants. Not to mention at Easter, Christmas, New Year and christenings, as well as holidays, barbecues, parties and social events. I would drink when watching the football, drink to relieve stress, to help calm me down and to relax me after a hard day. I would drink with meals, the odd glass of wine in the bath and (not forgetting) the ones for a little "Dutch courage". As you see, I only drank as little as any other *normal* drinker who is in *control!*

But was I ever really *choosing* to drink on these occasions, or did I *have* to in order to have a good time? Had my freedom of choice already been taken from me? It was this thinking that led me to question whether I even wanted to be in control. I started to realise that I was using some degree of willpower and discipline on a weekly, if not daily, basis to stop me drinking too much. Does this mean that I was in control of my alcohol intake because I could seemingly control it at times? Or does it simply mean that I was in a constant battle to gain control? I started to ask myself *"if you consciously have to keep control to make sure you do not drink too much then surely you cannot be in control?"* I now realise that of course I was never in true control of my alcohol intake and that nobody who drinks alcohol is ever really in control.

For the first time since just before I started drinking, I now have full control once more. The reason is because I no longer have to exercise control. It is the exercising of control, which proves that the addict is *not* in control.

Confused? I apologise. I'm racing ahead of myself. There is a lot of brainwashing and conditioning to be removed before you can even start to understand, let alone accept what I am saying. All I ask you to do whilst you read this book is to open your mind as much as possible and come with me as we explore the myths about the most used and accepted drug addiction in the world.

ALCOHOL ADDICTION

You may be asking yourself at this stage what makes me, Jason Vale, so qualified to write such a book? What reasons should you have for acting upon my advice, following my instructions, or even listening to what I have to say? What qualifications do I have? What is my medical background? After all, there are many books written by ex-drinkers offering advice on how to '*give up*' drinking. What makes me so different? Why should you follow my advice, when I am not as medically or perhaps even as academically qualified as these other people?

The difference is that I am **FREE!**

Yes FREE. (Let me be very clear on this point) I am not 'in recovery', not missing out, not pining for drink, or feeling deprived. I am not feeling miserable because I am not drinking, opting out of life, or attending sessions every week, and......no, I haven't found religion! I mean free, really FREE.

The freedom that I now have and the mental tools that helped me achieve it are what make me so qualified to help all *Alcohol Addicts*. I read several books on how to stop drinking when I was a drinker. But they were such diatribes of doom and gloom. In fact, if non-drinkers were to read some of them it would probably have driven them to drink! Every single book I read was written either by an "ex-alcoholic" (their terms, not mine) or by a doctor who was a DRINKER! The "ex-alcoholic" would be complaining from the start, informing you from page one that you have an incurable disease and describing how you will have to spend the rest of your life in 'recovery'. Oh what fun, hardly inspiring! As for the doctor, or anyone giving advice on how to do something when they haven't done it themselves, is ludicrous. How can any body give advice on how to stop drinking when they are still drinking? It would be equivalent to '*The Easy Way To Sparkling Wit and Repartee*' by William Hague. It just wouldn't wash!

Some doctors constitute, '*the "state the obvious" brigade.*' Please do not misread what I am saying, I am not criticising doctors professionally, but there are members of the medical profession who tend to state what the drinker already knows, eg:-

"You're drinking too much. You really should cut down or perhaps stop all together. Alcohol is killing you, destroying your life and causing you and your family all kinds of heartache"

Telling the alcohol addict what they are already fully aware of insults their intelligence. Imagine sinking in quicksand while somebody walks past and says "You should get out of there you know, you're sinking. Unless you get out you will probably die!" That sounds ridiculous I know, but no more ridiculous than the doctor who tells somebody who already knows that they are drinking too much, that they are drinking too much! One of the times when a drinker will reach for a drink is when they feel under pressure or stressed out, so putting pressure on people to stop drinking has the opposite effect.

I must emphasise again that I am not condemning doctors, they are in their profession to help people. Some doctors may strongly believe that by listing the reasons for stopping drinking it might help someone to quit or at least cut down on their consumption.

This approach may sound logical, but as you will discover in this book, everything about alcohol that appears logical is, in reality, the complete opposite.

For example, members of the organisation 'Drinkline' are considered one of the leading experts in helping people to stop drinking. They offer one piece of advice which on the surface sounds like good logical advice but is in fact the opposite;

'Note down all the reasons you can think of for stopping drinking'

Sounds logical, sounds like good advice, but if we question it for just a second we soon discover that it is far from good advice. Writing down all the reasons why you shouldn't drink will not make it easier for you to stop drinking, just as writing down all the reasons why you shouldn't be in quicksand will not make it easier for you to stop sinking.

Alcohol addicts already know all the reasons why they shouldn't drink. Bringing these facts to the forefront of their minds will not make it easier to stop. Most of the time it has the opposite effect. Let me explain why.

Firstly, those people who are in the advanced stages of alcohol addiction are constantly being pressured by loved ones, their doctors or society in general to stop drinking, or at least cut down their intake of alcohol. All this does is cause resentment. Nobody likes being told what to do by anybody else. The drinker feels an immediate sense of sacrifice and a strong feeling of deprivation is created by the situation. The more deprived they feel the *more* they will want a drink. The more they want the drink the more deprived they feel.

Secondly, a common mistake that people make when they make an attempt to stop drinking is to focus on all the reasons why they should not drink. They come up with list after list of reasons why they *should not* be doing it...

Health	**Money**	**Children**	**Family**
Hangovers	**Slavery**	**Violence**	**Arguments**
Lethargy	**Weight**	**Etc.**	

However, as mentioned, drinkers already know all the reasons why they should not drink. The truth, however, is that people do not drink alcohol for these reasons but for what they feel are the positive benefits eg, ... the pleasure, as a "crutch", to help calm them down, help them to relax, to give them confidence and courage, to make them happy and merry etc...

Just so you know what is in store, this book is not going to be a long drawn out lecture on why people should not drink, you already know the reasons. This book will be very different from the usual "doom and gloom" approach of 'giving up' drinking. By this, I mean the approach where the horrors of drink are explained so that the addict will hopefully stop out of fear. Once they *have* stopped they are then told that they are never really cured, but will have to spend the rest of their lives in something called '*recovery*'! No wonder they feel all doom and gloomy when they stop, so would I, if I thought I would have to suffer forever and that freedom was unachievable!

Not only is freedom possible, but it is also easy and extremely enjoyable to achieve. Once you fully understand how the confidence trick works, not only will you not envy people who drink, but you will look at them as you might now a heroin addict and genuinely pity them! I am fully aware that there are many people reading this book that have lost a great deal, suffered greatly at the hands of alcohol and desperately need to stop. However, people like this are not unique or alone. I have had best friends die because of alcohol. I have seen mental and physical abuse in my own family because of alcohol. I have had two family members literally drink their lives away, (one at the prime age of forty-nine) because of alcohol. I have spent nights in prison because of alcohol. I have lost relationships because of alcohol. I have also lost jobs because of alcohol. I have watched friends and family who have suffered physically and mentally because of alcohol. I have seen people lose their eyes, literally, because of alcohol. I have seen people disfigured for life with broken bottles as a direct result of drinking. We all know the horror stories and, as you will discover, there is hardly a single person on this planet who hasn't been either directly or indirectly abused by the drug called alcohol. Despite my previous experience, I now hold the view that the past is the past, and that no matter what alcohol has done it is now time to move on. I am also aware that there are many people reading this book that are not that desperate, have never really thought about stopping drinking forever, and believe that they are in control.

For years I never thought about stopping drinking either, for one reason and one reason alone – FEAR! As I have mentioned, the thought of never drinking ever again didn't just make me nervous, it petrified me! I now know that all alcohol addicts are just as scared as I was of stopping drinking and it is fear that actually keeps them hooked. Whether it's a drinker who is really desperate to stop, or someone who just wants to stop because they are fed up with drinking, the fears are the same for everyone. It is only fear that prevents them from doing the very simple task of stopping drinking. It was not the physical withdrawal that I was scared of, but the fear that I would never be able to enjoy or cope with my life the same way again without alcohol. All kinds of thoughts would go through my mind when I thought to myself 'I should *give up* drinking'. I would get butterflies in my stomach and my mind would race. I would think of every possible future scenario with me in it and no alcohol. It was not a pretty picture. Every image was of me standing with a coke, feeling miserable and deprived. I strongly feared that social gatherings would never be the same again. I feared becoming a social outcast. I felt that I wouldn't even want to go out if I couldn't drink. What would I do on my Birthday? What about Christmas, New Year, holidays?? The biggest fear I had is that I could see that the craving for alcohol would never go. I thought that I would have to use willpower and discipline not to drink *forever*! I was as confused as hell. The truth was that I thought I wanted to *stop* drinking, but I wanted to drink as well. That is why I was never sure if I really *wanted* to stop altogether.

Since I stopped drinking I can now see very clearly that it is fear that prevents people from getting free. And don't you have some of these fears too? Doesn't the thought of NEVER having a drink EVER again put a certain amount of fear into you or maybe even complete and utter terror? These fears keep people drinking and make them block their minds to the health, money, hangovers, slavery, and the effects on their families and friends.

However, what all *Alcohol Addicts* fail to realise (and what I failed to realise a few years ago) is that ALL of those fears are only caused by one thing and one thing alone – the alcohol itself. People who do not drink alcohol do not have these fears. Before you started drinking *you* did not have these fears. I no longer have these fears.

I now want to scream from the rooftops and tell the world that they really do not need to drink alcohol; they just *think* that they do. The need for alcohol is *caused* by alcohol and it's easy to stop once you realise that there are *no* genuine benefits in drinking alcohol.

Come with me on a fun and exciting journey to remove the brainwashing, conditioning and all of the illusions so that once you have a full understanding of the alcohol trap, all of your fears will be removed forever.

At this stage you may strongly believe that you do not want to become a *non*-drinker; I understand this fully. All I ask is that you read this book with an open mind and you just may start to think differently. You have nothing to lose. When I say an open mind, I mean really open it as wide as possible. A few years ago I would probably have dismissed most of what is in this book. The only way your perception of the drug alcohol can possibly change is if, just while you read this book, you put aside all of your beliefs about alcohol. Forget everything that you have ever been taught about alcohol. Forget everything that your parents have taught you, everything that your doctor has told you and everything that you have told yourself about alcohol. Many people believed that the world was flat at one stage; it took somebody with an open mind to see through that perception to the truth. Once the illusions and brainwashing have been eliminated you will enjoy your life so much more without alcohol. I do not simply mean that you will be richer and healthier; I mean that you will not miss drinking. You will have more courage and confidence and, far from having a void in your life when you stop, you will feel more fulfilled than you have felt in years. As impossible or as daunting as that may sound at the moment, once you understand the nature of the trap, it would be hard to convince you otherwise. In fact it would be hard to persuade you to drink again!

However, there is a lot of brainwashing and conditioning to be removed before we reach that stage.

In order for you to find your way out of the 'alcohol trap' you need to do a few things:

1. Read this book with a very open mind
2. Read ALL of the book in order (don't dip in)
3. Follow my guidelines

The first guideline is to continue drinking until you have finished reading this book. Now let me make myself clear here, I don't mean get plastered every time you read the book! It just means do not make an attempt to stop drinking until all of the brainwashing has been completely removed. If you have already stopped drinking prior to picking up this book, but feel as though you are still not free, i.e., you still miss drinking and feel deprived by not drinking, then this book will enable you to get truly free. However, if you have stopped already for a length of time then DO NOT, I repeat **DO NOT** start drinking again. Read the book with an open mind and your mental cravings will be gradually destroyed as you make your way through the book. But if you are still drinking then continue as 'normal' until you have completed the book.

There may well be several points in the book that make you see the light, but please do not stop until you have completely finished the book as you need to have a full understanding of all the possible pitfalls. Perhaps the most important guideline of them all is to actually finish the book! Do not let fear prevent you from completing this book. It is time to break through your fears and find freedom.

Every point I make in this book is for a reason. Every point is here to make absolutely certain that you succeed *permanently*. Success means freedom and freedom means not pining for a drink ever again, not feeling deprived, not opting out of life, and not getting angry or upset that you are not drinking. If you read this book with your mind as open as the universe *and* follow my guidelines, you will achieve what I have achieved – TRUE FREEDOM FROM HAVING TO DRINK ALCOHOL.

You will find that some of the points in the book are repeated. I make no apologies for this at all. The message in this book is very simple. Understanding the alcohol trap is simplicity itself, but in order for it to gel fully in your mind, some of the key fundamental points are repeated throughout the book; almost like a form of hypnosis and are repeated on purpose. We have a lot to get through so lets get started by immediately removing a huge chunk of the brainwashing, the belief that if people are not alcoholics, then they are in control of their drinking. So, the first question that people ask themselves when they think they can no longer control their drinking is…

2

Am I An Alcoholic?

And the simple answer is NO you are not. Never have been and never will be. The reason I know this is because, as mentioned already, there is no such thing as an alcoholic, as society understands it, and there is no such illness as alcoholism.

I realise that is a pretty bold statement to make, but I assure you that it is an accurate one. In fact it's the brainwashing from organisations like A.A. (Alcoholics Anonymous) that create the myth that there is a disease called alcoholism. Please do not misunderstand, I believe that Alcoholics Anonymous have clearly helped thousands of people. People who would have been destroyed and some that would no longer be here if it weren't for A.A. The constant commitment and help they give to alcohol addicts around the world, around the clock, is to be greatly admired. The problem is, however well intentioned their motives may be, they suggest to the alcohol addict that he has an incurable disease. In fact, A.A. state that there is NO cure for the disease known as alcoholism. By their own admission, A.A. has never cured a single *Alcoholic!*

Put yourself in the position of thinking that you may be an alcoholic. You need help. So where do you go? Well, first of all you need to know for certain if you have the disease (alcoholism). The first thing you do is to consult your doctor. Your doctor cannot tell you if you *are* an alcoholic but refer you to A.A., Drink Line, Alcohol Concern or whatever 'expert' organisation happens to be to hand. Next, you phone one of these organisations to find out if you have the disease. The problem is that nobody can let you know if you have this disease. A.A., for example, simply state the following in one of their official booklets;

"If you repeatedly drink more than you intend or want to, or if you get into trouble when you drink, you may be an alcoholic. Only you can decide. No one in A.A. will tell you whether you are or not."

So even A.A., who claims to be the world's leading experts on coping with alcoholism, cannot tell you if you have a disease that they seemingly invented! So who can? Well, nobody, apparently, only *you* can decide. Now that does not exactly inspire me with confidence from the start. Only *I* can decide if I have this disease? They, the people who created this 'alcoholism' disease cannot tell me?

So, if we do have to decide for ourselves, what guidelines do we have to go on? Well, according to A.A. if you repeatedly drink more than you intend to or want to, or if you get into trouble when you are drunk, then you may be an alcoholic. Are they kidding? There isn't one person who drinks alcohol that doesn't repeatedly drink more than they intend to ... it's the nature of the drug! And as for getting into trouble when you have been drinking, hasn't everybody who drinks got into trouble at some point in their lives because of drink? Of course they have! So according to A.A.'s official booklet, if we take *their* guidelines, EVERYBODY who drinks alcohol may be an alcoholic! That would mean that ninety percent of this country was born with a disease for which there is no known cure. I have only one thing to say to that –

BULLSHIT!

Did you know that alcoholism is now included in the same category as cancer, and heart disease! Some people even claim that you inherit it, it's in your genes and there is nothing you can do about it. There are even people who claim that they can tell if somebody is an alcoholic by the time they are TWO years old. Some people believe that there are alcoholics that have never touched a drop of alcohol in their lives. Yes, they believe there are people who have never drunk alcohol that have this disease! What I want you to do during this book is to question this kind of clear rubbish. We end up believing them because we have been conditioned to accept them as correct. But once you start to question them, they just don't make sense. Use your common sense. Do you believe that heroin addicts have a disease called heroinism? Or that they are heroinolics? (Nothing to do with the drug, you understand, they were born with a disease called heroinism and can do nothing about it!) Do you honestly believe that there are people out there who are heroin addicts, and who have never taken heroin in their lives? Do you believe for a second that there are smokers out there who have never had a cigarette? Do you think that you can tell whether someone will take crack cocaine by the time they are two years old? Do you honestly believe that you inherit these addictions, that they are in your genes? Do you believe that people who are addicted to chocolate were born with a disease? A disease which meant that they would have to eat chocolate all of their lives and could do NOTHING about it? When you were two years old did you say *"thank God I can communicate properly, now I can talk I can ask for a drink. I've been gagging for one for two years!!!?"*

All I ask of you during this book is to use **your common sense** and actually *question* this nonsense. I know that we have heard this clap trap for years, but just because they are put across by 'experts' does not make it the truth. Open your mind and use your own judgement to come to an intelligent conclusion. If you have been labeled with the title alcoholic yourself and it has become part of who you are, then I urge you to open your mind and ask *how can there be any such thing as an alcoholic?* It is time to see the truth. The word *alcoholic* is just a label put on people who realise they are hooked. It is time to get rid of this ridiculous label, because that is all it is....*a label!*

The fact is that you are not an alcoholic, (regardless of what you may have been told) because there is no such thing. However, if you take alcohol on a regular basis then you are an alcohol addict and you are hooked on alcohol. So what's the difference?

The difference is that there is an easy, straightforward cure for alcohol addiction (you're reading it) and according to its creators there is no known cure for alcoholism!

In reality, everyone who drinks alcohol on a regular basis is in exactly the same position – HOOKED! It doesn't matter if they only drink at weekends, or whether they drink all day, everyday, they are hooked and addicted to a drug called alcohol.

It is easy to understand this addiction with other drugs. If somebody takes heroin, they are a heroin addict, if somebody takes crack cocaine, they are a 'crack head', if somebody smokes, they are a nicotine addict. Would you change your view if the person taking heroin says,

"I'm not addicted to heroin. I'm in full control. I don't need it all the time. I can do without it. It's not like I take it ALL the time. I'll prove I don't have a problem with heroin. I only take it at weekends, and special occasions, and if I'm feeling a bit stressed out! What's more I cannot be addicted because I don't take heroin in the morning"

If you heard someone voicing this, would you think that they were clearly *not* addicted and in full control of their intake of heroin? Would you believe that they could take heroin whenever they liked without getting hooked? Or would you know for certain that they are **already** addicted and simply trying to justify how *'little'* of the drug they are **already** taking?

It is so obvious. You would realise that this person was already hooked and you would see clearly that they were not in control. It would be obvious to everyone, except perhaps the addict themselves. Why is this *not* the case with the drug alcohol? Why can't people see that they are addicted to alcohol? The reason why it isn't that evident is because **NINETY PERCENT** of the U.K. drinks alcohol! If ninety percent of the population took heroin, if it were legal and we had been conditioned since birth to believe that shooting up heroin was a natural pastime, then it's possible that heroin taking would not be seen as drug addiction either. It is possible that we might actually believe that imbibing heroin was normal? At the same time we need to remember that virtually everybody who tries to offer advice on alcohol addiction take drugs themselves. The biggest sales force that the alcohol industry has are the *alcohol addicts*. It was only the influence of other drinkers that got us into drinking alcohol in the first place. We simply end up believing what we have been told. The illusions which alcohol creates simply confirm what we have been conditioned to believe.

So the poor drinker, even if he thinks he is drinking too much and has started to become conscious of the reality that he is not actually in control and wants to quit, is immediately labelled with this term – alcoholic. If you are not an alcoholic, what possible reason could you have for even wanting to stop? The drinker is then left in what they see as a no win situation, either tell the world that they are not in control of alcohol, or lie about their intake and carry on drinking with their heads in the sand. The problem is, that unlike smoking where people can openly express a desire to stop, the drinker has to put up a front and lie or otherwise say they are an alcoholic. What a choice! It is the only drug in the world that has this division depending on just how much of the drug is taken. The difference between *normal* and *alcoholism*. But at what point do you become an alcoholic? How much do you need to drink per day to qualify for the title? How much heroin does a person have to take before they are hooked? When do you progress from heroin user to heroinolic? How much cocaine do you need to take before you get the disease cocaineism? How many cigarettes do you need to smoke each day before you go from *normal* smoker to smokeaholic?

People feel so ashamed to mention that they have realised that they are no longer in control and would like to stop drinking. *They* are seen as the problem and not the drug. With all other drug addiction it's the other way around. Smokers voice all the time that they would love to stop yet are never branded with an outrageous title like nicotineolic! The main problem is that if you sense that you are in trouble with alcohol, it is seen as *your* weakness, rather than a result of the drug itself.

I remember when I was growing up, constantly seeing an image of a heroin addict lying on a floor in a darkened room saying *"I can handle it"*. It was on television all the time, *'I can handle it'*. I remember thinking how pathetic that heroin addict looked and how ridiculous that the remark sounded, *"I can handle it"*, *"I can control it"*. Yet I kept saying the same nonsense when I was hooked on alcohol. It seemed normal to me. We have been brainwashed to believe that either you are out of control with alcohol (which means that you are either a weak-willed jellyfish or probably an alcoholic) or, you are in full control of what you are doing. What a choice! What position would you choose to say that you are in? I know which option I would rather choose, the one I chose for years. The same one that all alcohol addicts use *"I can control my drinking. I might drink a bit too much on occasions, but I am of course in control"*. You see apparently that is the difference between alcoholics and *'normal drinkers'*, alcoholics have lost control, whereas normal drinkers are in control.

RUBBISH!

Have you ever seen anybody who is drunk in control of their actions? It is a contradiction in terms. And what is meant by *'normal drinkers'*? If I kept saying to you that I was in full control of my banana intake, that I only have them a few times week, I can take them or leave them, I have more at weekends, but then doesn't everybody? That I can even go two complete days without bananas, wouldn't you immediately know that I was *out* of control with my bananas? Doesn't the mere fact that I am trying to justify how little I take, prove that the bananas are indeed controlling me? Doesn't it really mean that I have to exercise discipline and control to try and keep in control of my intake? What I am saying is, if I said that about my banana intake I *would* have a problem and you would know it!

A.D.S

There are some *experts* now who do not use the term *'alcoholic'* and say that people who are not in control of their drinking have 'Alcohol Dependency Syndrome'. But doesn't *everybody* who drinks alcohol on a regular basis have 'alcohol dependency syndrome'? Don't all heroin addicts have 'Heroin Dependency Syndrome'? Or smokers 'Nicotine

Dependency Syndrome'? What I mean is that *anybody* who drinks alcohol 'depends' on it, they feel as though they 'need' it at certain times in order to cope, or enjoy themselves. They feel as though they wouldn't enjoy themselves in certain situations without alcohol. Clearly, a dependency is there and that is why there is such a fear of stopping altogether. If people didn't feel as though they depended on it, then everybody would find it easy to stop drinking whenever they wanted, but you and I know that even going 'on the wagon' can be hell. 'Experts' state that if you are not in control you have 'dependency syndrome'. I am stating categorically that nobody is ever in total control of their intake. So therefore *everybody* who drinks must have Alcohol Dependency Syndrome. It is not a *choice* for the drinker, it is *necessity*!

"Either the drink goes or I do"

Some people will say this as a way of hopefully getting their drinking partners to quit. This rarely, if ever, works as the drinker will choose the drink over their partners! Not because the drink is their genuine choice, or because they do not love their partners, but because the decision is being made for them. Their judgement and rational thinking is always 'under influence' – the often subconscious influence of alcohol.

The first thing that I need you to realise is that people who drink alcohol on a regular basis are not in control of their drinking and that they are hooked. Just because so many believe that they are indeed in full control, does not actually make it true. It is never possible to be in true control of any drug, the drug will always be controlling its victim, whether the victim realises it or not. The biggest gain in stopping drinking is to be free from the constant battle to try and keep control. I will explain more about this controlling factor later in the book. This kind of brainwashing has caused people to feel ashamed if they have had to seek help to quit alcohol. In fact, while you are reading this book you may, at times, be hiding the cover from people, or not telling people about your intentions. The irony is that the people you are hiding it from are probably drinkers themselves!

There is such a stigma in admitting that you are hooked on alcohol and need help, this *must* be changed. People on the whole have very little idea that they are hooked. In fact many alcohol addicts have lived and died without ever realising this. For many years people had no idea that they were hooked on cigarettes. It was only when smoking became anti-social and was banned in many public places that smokers became aware of their addiction. They soon realised that they were not *choosing* to smoke, but *had* to smoke. Most drinkers, however, are unaware of this. They believe that if they are managing to control their intake, then they are *in* control. However, what happened with prohibition, where all alcohol was banned? It resulted in organised crime. It soon became clear that people were not choosing to drink they *had* to drink. Would the same thing have happened if they had banned bananas? The brainwashing, conditioning and illusions created by alcohol, has caused a situation where people strongly believe that they cannot live without it. I used to strongly believe that I was choosing to drink and I could stop whenever I wanted, I never really thought that I was hooked. But if that were really the case then why did I find it hard to stop for more than a week and why did the thought of stopping drinking fill me with fear?

The hard truth is that alcohol is a drug and one hell of an addictive one at that. And like any drug, its nature is to drag you further and further into its life subtle life and soul destroying clutches. However, contrary to the brainwashing that organisations like A.A. put out, and despite the collective belief amongst drinkers that life just wouldn't be worth living without the most heavily advertised drug on the planet, there is some very good news for anyone caught in the alcohol trap.....

3

It's Easy To Stop Drinking

 Not only is it easy to stop drinking, but the process of stopping is enjoyable and it is easy to stay stopped. That is precisely what this book is all about, showing you just how easy it can be to stop drinking and stay stopped. This can be achieved without the need for willpower, discipline or feelings of deprivation and misery. The truth is that it has always been easy to stop drinking alcohol. We have been conditioned to believe otherwise. The problem I had when I tried to quit was that I approached it in the wrong way for so long that I convinced myself that it was difficult to stop. At the same time, society has taught us that it is not only difficult, but also *impossible* to achieve true freedom from alcohol. This is another reason why people look to cut down or try to control rather than stop altogether, for what is the point in trying to escape from prison when you have been conditioned to believe that there is no possible chance of escape? The next best thing is to make prison life somehow more bearable.

I made several attempts to stop drinking. Well, when I say stop, I guess I mean cut down. The thought of actually quitting alcohol FOREVER put the fear of God into me. I would often go 'on the wagon' just to prove that I wasn't hooked and that I was in control. But surely just going on the wagon to try and prove that I was not hooked was proof in itself that I definitely was! There is a book out at the moment called '*How To Stop Drinking For A Month*'. At the start of this book the author states that alcohol is the most wonderful thing on the planet, that you will definitely miss drinking, and that you will find it very difficult to stop. However, he suggests you should stop for a month every now and then, just to prove that you are in control! **In control?!** What is he talking about? You have just brought a book explaining how to *give up* drinking for a month, surely that alone should be proof in itself that you are *not* in control. If you were in control and could genuinely take it or leave it, you would simply stop doing it. You certainly wouldn't need the help of a book would you?

I would never have believed a few years ago that it was not only easy to stop drinking, but that I would ever contemplate stopping drinking forever, enjoy the process and never miss it. However, that is exactly what has happened and I now want to show the world *exactly* how we have all been fooled so that they too can find freedom, gain true control and achieve what is apparently impossible. For, as I have mentioned, people who realise that they are in the alcohol trap and want to get out are led to believe that they are somehow different than '*normal*' drinkers and that *they* have lost control. These people are then immediately branded with the title **ALCOHOLIC!** We are taught that you are born with that disease and you can never ever really be free. So why should you be happy when you stop? In the poor alcohol addict's mind there is nothing to be happy about. On the contrary, there is something to be very miserable about – a lifetime of misery. So we are conditioned and brainwashed, not only by our own attempts to stop, but also by society, that quitting alcohol and being completely free is **impossible** to achieve. We hear of people going into clinics to dry out for months and *still* not being free. Yet the beautiful truth is it is easy to stop drinking and not miss it for one reason alone – there is *nothing* to miss. It is all one huge lie that we have been conditioned to believe, not only by society, but also by the clever illusions created by the drug itself.

Why is it difficult to stop drinking? This should be the real question. After all, you don't even need to *do* anything; all you have to do is not drink alcohol! If you were trying to navigate your way around the world in a hot air balloon, *that* would be difficult. If you had to run a hundred metres in under ten seconds, then it might take years to reach the peak physical condition and even then you might not be physically capable of achieving it. So why do people, when they have reached the stage where they want to stop drinking, (knowing that it is slowly destroying them physically and mentally), find it difficult to achieve? It is simply because, although they strongly believe that alcohol is destroying them, they still think that alcohol provides some sort of genuine pleasure or crutch. They believe that there is still some benefit in taking alcohol. They have reached a stage where they believe that the disadvantages outweigh the advantages, but still believe that there are occasional advantages in drinking alcohol. While the alcohol addict believes that there is any genuine advantage in drinking alcohol, they will always find it very difficult to quit or feel miserable for the rest of their lives after they *have* quit. This is why it was so difficult for me during my three months 'on the wagon' experience. Once the illusions have been removed and the alcohol addict realises that they were tricked by an ingenious trap, then the penny finally drops that there are no advantages in drinking alcohol whatsoever. Then and only then is true freedom possible. If the illusions and years of brainwashing have not been fully removed and they *do* believe that they have made a genuine sacrifice then even if they do not drink, they will still *never* feel truly free. As mentioned, in order to get free from any trap you must realise you are in one. It is equally important to realise when you are free. Unfortunately the alcohol addict is told he can never get free, so of course he never feels free. In his mind he hasn't reached the stage where he is relieved that he does not need to drink anymore. He is always in the *process* of stopping drinking.

Some time ago I watched a programme where Paul Merson (English footballer), was being interviewed. The majority of the interview was about his drinking, or *not* drinking to be more precise. Paul is undoubtedly to be admired for what he has achieved after telling the world that he *is* an '*alcoholic*' The problem is that he doesn't know that he is free, because he doesn't *feel* free. Somebody gave him a label and told him that he can only ever expect a *satisfactory* way of life! They told him that he was going to have to battle for the rest of his life. In fact, in the interview he said that he was still taking one day at a time. No wonder we don't look forward to stopping drinking. Paul battled for over four years and has recently fallen 'off the wagon'. During those four years he felt as though he couldn't go out and have fun like everybody else. He was told that *he* was different. He felt different. He felt miserable and deprived about not being able to drink for FOUR YEARS! No wonder he eventually succumbed. I do not know whether Paul will be drinking or not when you read this book, but I can only hope that he has read this book and is now finally *free*. The alcohol trap is very simple and my only question is why did it take me so long to figure the whole thing out? It is easy to stop drinking and enjoyable to be free for the rest of your life (as you will discover) all we need to do is remove all of the brainwashing and conditioning because that is where the addiction *really* lies.

To be honest, some of the advice given by so-called experts on alcohol addiction perpetuates the illusion that you will find it difficult, or impossible to stop drinking. They imply that you will have to go through months of torture and that it won't be easy. "It's a long road ahead", they often say. Well perhaps it is if you go about it the wrong way, but then so is the Rubix cube until you discover the solution.

I have now in front of me 'Drink lines' official pamphlet on

'The effective strategies to help you cope with stopping drinking'

Look at the heading to start with, it states **"*cope with*"**. They are already implying that stopping drinking is difficult. Using the term 'cope with' suggests once again, that you can never be free, but that you can only come to terms with or *cope* with stopping drinking. They then proceed to give you a list of *'effective strategies'* to hinder you, (oh sorry I mean help you!). I have already mentioned one of these strategies which states;

"Note down all the reasons why you want to stop"

I previously explained why this strategy doesn't help people to stop drinking but in fact makes it harder to quit! Logically it should help, but everything about alcohol addiction that appears logical, is in fact the complete opposite. One of the times that an alcohol addict will reach for a drink is when he is stressed or under pressure. So listing down all the reasons why they shouldn't drink will simply remind them of what they already know and make them even more stressed and pressured than before they created the list! So what is the first thing they are likely to do? Have a drink to try and block their minds to what they already knew anyway! And as I have said, people do not drink for the reasons they **shouldn't** drink, but for the reasons they **do** drink. This piece of advice clearly doesn't help people to stop, no matter how many experts say otherwise, but let's explore some of their other *helpful strategies* mentioned in this pamphlet.

"Change your routine – perhaps choose different routes to the office or shops, avoiding pubs and off-licences"

In other words, they are suggesting that you remove temptation. This again seems logical advice, but it is nonsense. They are telling you that you should somehow avoid the TWO HUNDRED THOUSAND pubs and off-licences that are to be found in the U.K. on your way to the office or shops. If you do go into shops therefore, you must avoid the ones selling alcohol, otherwise you will be open to temptation and failing to follow their instructions. Presumably you shouldn't watch television or listen to the radio either as alcohol is often being advertised on them. The programmes themselves are always advocating that drink is pleasurable and marvellous, so you might be tempted if you watch or listen to them and again you would be failing to follow *their* strategy. Do not go out ever again, as you may be tempted to drink in the company of other people who are drinking! You may have also had alcohol with a meal, so never eat again! Think about it, how *can* you avoid temptation if you still want to drink? When I drank, every lunchtime, every meal, every evening, every day I was TEMPTED. So in order not to be tempted you should never wake up. Even then you might be dreaming about having a drink. IF YOU STILL **WANT** TO DRINK THEN YOU WILL BE TEMPTED NO MATTER WHERE YOU WALK TO OR FROM!

'Discover different ways to relax'

Different ways to relax? This is another huge part of the brainwashing (which we will destroy later); they are implying that alcohol genuinely relaxes you. The beautiful truth is that you won't need to find different ways to relax as you will be far more relaxed as a non-drinker anyway. It is alcohol that CAUSES you to feel un-relaxed in the first place! *(I will explain this later)*

'Take up old interests and activities you used to enjoy or explore new ones'

What old interests do they mean? I started drinking when I was at school, so I guess I should get out my skateboard instead of having a drink! This would prove very difficult to do whilst having a meal! This piece of advice perpetuates the fear that you will no longer be able to the same things you did as a drinker. It wouldn't be possible to go out socially, for example, which you will soon realise is clear rubbish.

'If you are thirsty, have a long soft drink – *'keep plenty of soft drinks easily available'*

If you are thirsty have a drink. Really? Thank you and (don't tell me) if I get hungry I should eat too, right? Maybe I should keep plenty of food easily available as well. Pathetic!

'Try different types of soft drinks – *you may like them!*

Oh come on. If you do not have anything constructive to say, say

NOTHING at all. Do they think that we are children? In fact, would you dream of telling your child something so patently obvious? There I was, an alcohol addict for years and all I had to do was drink soft drinks instead of alcoholic ones and my problem would have been solved, why didn't *I* think of that?!

'Do something whilst you drink at a social venue such as play darts, bingo or dance'

Are they on a wind up with this one? PLAY DARTS! Of course there is ample proof to show that playing darts helps people to stop or cut down on drinking. I mean you have only got to look at the top darts players to see that!

'Prepare yourself – *rehearse saying "NO" to offers of alcoholic drinks.*

Yes you read correctly. In fact they go one stage further and ask you to stand in front of a mirror and rehearse saying "NO". They actually suggest ways that you should do it as well: *"No thanks, maybe next time." "No thanks, I'm driving". "Not now".* Can you imagine what an idiot you would feel doing that? They also suggest that you rehearse with a friend! Friend! You would have no friends left if you started doing that. The friends you would have wouldn't be much help either as all they would be able to say is "Hey nonney nonney" and their arms would be permanently stuck behind their backs encased in a white jacket!

'Take each day at a time'

First of all it's a ridiculous statement to make anyway *'take each day as it comes',* how else can you live your life? Whether you drink or not you have no choice but to take each day as it comes. I dare you *not* to take each day at a time! But the main problem with this *'strategy'* is that it strongly gives the impression that the drinker will have to battle for the rest of his life, ALL DAY, EVERYDAY! Always having to *cope* one day at a time without drink. There are people who have been going to A.A. meetings for over twenty years and still stand up and say "I am Albert, I am an Alcoholic." How on earth can they be an alcoholic, they haven't had a drink for over TWENTY YEARS! I have always thought that the way to recognise an *'alcoholic'* is someone who drinks to excess on a regular basis. Someone who drinks first thing in the morning or somebody who cannot cope without a drink. Albert hasn't had a drink in 20 YEARS, how the hell can he be an *'alcoholic'*? Paul Merson himself said during that interview that he was 'taking each day as it comes' and that he was going to have to battle and suffer for the rest of his life.

SUFFER? BATTLE? With what? I suffered too. But that was when I *WAS* drinking....not now! One of the biggest joys of being free is not to have to battle any longer to try to gain control, not to have to use willpower or discipline over my intake of the drug, or suffer mentally and physically because of alcohol ever again.

This is one of the major mistakes that people make when they stop drinking, they start counting the days. They are waiting everyday to see whether or not they fail!

No wonder people don't look forward to quitting. We are constantly conditioned to believe that you can never truly get free, that you will *always* have to battle.

RUBBISH!

Alcohol addicts can get truly free and it is easy. The truth is that they already know that it's easy to stop drinking, if you think about it, they actually do that every time they finish a drink. The problem is not picking up the next one and the one after that and the hundreds, if not thousands after that.

This is the main bone of contention that I have with organisations like Drink Line and A.A. They imply that **you** are making a genuine sacrifice. That **you** will be missing out on some sort of genuine pleasure or crutch, and isn't it a shame that you have a problem with drink and will never be able to drink 'normally' again. In the interview with Paul Merson, Paul was asked what he would do when the F.A.Cup was passed around with champagne in it. Paul sheepishly said "*I would just pass it on and have a lemonade*". This question was odd for two reasons. Firstly, why ask the question? It seems strange to ask somebody who you *know* doesn't drink alcohol what he would do with champagne. It would be like asking a vegetarian, what they would do if offered a piece of meat! What did he expect Paul Merson to do? Carry on celebrating I would imagine, (like everybody else) on winning the most important trophy in English football. The question was inappropriate for another reason. The real question should have been "Do you think that you will win the F.A.Cup" or "How would it feel to win the cup?" Why does drink even enter into it? That part of his life was OVER (or so you would think). But it wasn't, because in his mind he was *still* not free. He was effectively pining for something which he hoped he would never have again!

He stopped drinking for over four years, there was NO trace of the drug in his body, yet he and many like him are still suffering after they have stopped. Some people haven't had a drink in years and are still pining for a drink and feeling miserable because they are not drinking, they are still fighting a desire to drink. But where is the physical addiction? Open your mind and ask yourself this question. We have been told that the physical addiction is where the problem lies. But is it? When *alcohol addicts* go into a clinic to 'DRY OUT' for six weeks, they come out with no trace of alcohol in their system, yet still have the mental desire to drink. Most people, who go through the awful experience of going to a drying out clinic, usually have a drink within the first week of leaving! When I stopped for those three months, the desire or craving for a drink got WORSE! If it *were* the physical addiction to alcohol that caused the craving for the drug, then I would have been free after only a few days. Alcohol itself leaves the body very quickly. This is essential as it is a powerful poison and if the body stored it you would die! In fact **every trace of alcohol has gone after the first week to ten days**. I will repeat this medical fact for those who have been conditioned to believe otherwise:-

Every trace of alcohol has gone from the addict's system within seven to ten days after their last drink!

So *why* anybody needs to 'dry out' for six weeks is a complete mystery. You may already know that there are certain drugs, like Disulphiram, which are taken to help keep people off alcohol. If you take Disulphiram and drink just a tiny amount of alcohol it can make you acutely ill. The drug (apparently) should be continued until the craving for alcohol is lost. Let me ask you a question, is their any sense whatsoever in taking a drug to get off another drug? If you are thinking that it works for heroin, think again. Methadone (the drug used to solve heroin addiction) kills more people than heroin! It does not *cure* the addiction, it simply *moves* the problem, it does not *re-move* it!

It is ludicrous to think that this kind of approach would be effective in stopping people drinking at all. It is suggested that if you take the drug Disulphiram and drink alcohol you may become acutely ill. ACUTELY ILL? If you are hooked on alcohol and somebody says to you "Here, have this drug. After you take it you will not be allowed to drink alcohol. If you do it will make you feel ill!" What do you think you would do? You wouldn't stop drinking, you would stop taking Disulphirum! Drinkers are not put off by becoming ill, acutely or otherwise. Every drinker has suffered with a humdinger of a hangover at least once, does that stop them?

As for the advice on continuing with the drug until the craving has gone, how long would they expect you to be on this drug? According to them the craving never goes, so the answer must be – FOREVER! The craving is not physical. The reality is that if you put a drug in your body which prevented you from drinking alcohol at all, then you would crave it even more. The problem is **not** physical. The craving is **NOT** physical, and (just in case you missed it), it's not physical – it's *psychological*. The problem is the way the drug is perceived in the addict's mind. I never suffered physically when I was 'on the wagon'; I was suffering mentally because I felt *deprived* of something that I wanted. I was miserable in my mind, not body! I was in a tantrum, rather like a child who is not allowed to have his or her toy. I was suffering from "mental deprivation" and nothing more than that.

I'm not saying for a second that *some* alcohol addicts (those who drink heavily from morning till night usually) don't have a degree of withdrawal. In fact for some their sugar levels are so shot and body so starved of nutrients, that yes, they do indeed suffer physically when suddenly cut off the supply of this liquid drug. But even in the most severe cases the sugar levels and nutrients can *easily* be solved with the power of some delicious pints of raw juice and super fruit smoothies (for all info on this aspect please get hold of *The Juice Master's Ultimate Fast Food* book). But for the *vast* majority of people reading this book there just isn't any withdrawal. I mean exactly what physical withdrawal are we talking about here? Where exactly will it hurt? What does it amount to really? A hangover? How long does that last? We have all had our fair share of those and we have all got over them too. The alcohol addict who has reached the stage where he has lost his home, job, and family (all for the precious nectar), will not have endured all that heartache through fear of a hangover. The fear for every alcohol addict is that they will not enjoy or cope with their lives in the same way without alcohol. The only thing that keeps people hooked on alcohol are the illusions in the *mind* created by the drug itself and the years of conditioning and brainwashing. That is why I am so excited to share this information with you. It is what makes this approach of stopping so easy and enjoyable. Alcohol addicts are only hooked on what they have been brainwashed to believe that alcohol does for them. The chemical effect of alcohol creates the illusions which seem to confirm all of the brainwashing. All we have to do is remove the brainwashing then the addiction is automatically removed. I am fully aware that if you have tried for years to break free and found it difficult, then even accepting what I am saying at this stage may be difficult too. I am not asking you just to accept everything that I am saying, I want you to be sceptical, and to question not only your own views on alcohol but more importantly what society has led you to believe. I am also fully aware that there will be several people who are reading this book who have never really considered stopping and perhaps believe that they are not hooked. It really doesn't matter which category you fall into, providing that you **open your mind,** this book will change the way you look and think about the drug called alcohol forever.

So if the addiction is over 90% psychological and only about 10% physical (if that), then in order to break free, all we need to do is remove the brainwashing and make sure you have some live nutrients flowing through your system during the first week or so to help with any 'hangover' from the addiction.

We need to understand not why people *shouldn't* drink alcohol because we are all fully aware of that. The real question we should ask is .....

4

Why Do Peoplr Drink Alcohol?

The answer is because we have been conditioned and brainwashed to drink alcohol from a very early age.

Because of the illusions that alcohol creates, people strongly believe that there are genuine benefits in drinking alcohol. The sad reality is that it is so part of our identity as a nation. We have somehow reached the stage where it is now the only drug on the planet that if you *do not* take it, then you must either be suffering from a mythical disease known as alcoholism, or driving, or you are obviously some kind of FREAK!

If you stop smoking you are a hero, if you come off heroin you are congratulated on your achievement, but so strong is the brainwashing with alcohol that if you stop drinking, people think you need medical assistance for the rest of your life. WHY?

It may be because over *ninety percent* of our population are being conned by the same illusions and feel dependent on them. They know that just the *thought* of never drinking again instils them with such fear that they are convinced that stopping for good means suffering forever.

Alcohol really has everyone fooled. The brainwashing is so severe that it would be hard not to get hooked on alcohol with the amount of social pressure trying to get you hooked. Almost from the moment we are born we are constantly being bombarded with information telling us that alcohol, not only makes you an adult, but portraying alcohol addicts as heroes and heroines. The strong are made stronger, the weak are suddenly transformed into courageous and confident people because they drink alcohol. I don't suppose a single youngster, after seeing a 'tramp' drinking lighter fuel first thing in the morning, or watching somebody getting loud, argumentative, aggressive, abusive, nasty, violent, overemotional, obnoxious, stupid, or slumped over the toilet vomiting, has ever been even remotely tempted to try their first alcoholic drink. Why not? Because this is the *reality* of alcohol. Why should we be expected to relate to this side of it when we are constantly being bombarded with the other picture of drinking. These pictures show young, strong, wealthy, successful, and attractive people having a good time 'DRINKING'. Film stars, pop stars and successful businessmen and women. Doctors, lawyers, friends, family, partners ...... everyone it seems is constantly telling us that drinking is good for the mind and soul. We even have doctors telling us that alcohol is GOOD for you! (I will cover this later)

We have been conditioned to believe that *any* form of celebration must involve alcohol; otherwise it is not a celebration. Christmas, New Year, birthdays and christenings, (let's wet the babies head!), weddings, holidays, weekends, competition wins, new jobs, pay rises and engagements .... Let's drink to this, let's drink to that, in fact lets drink to anything as long as we DRINK!

TWO HUNDRED MILLION pounds is spent on advertising alcohol in the U.K. alone, every year. The government earns TEN BILLION pounds a year from alcohol. We as a nation spend nearly twenty five billion pounds on alcohol per year. That is more than the annual spend on clothes, schools and hospitals.

It seems strange that society is often very judgmental when it comes to other forms of drug addiction. Other forms of drug addiction that they are fortunate enough not to be addicted to! Before I understood the nature of drug addiction fully I would often be the first in line to judge drug addicts. I wasn't a drug addict myself, after all I only smoked and drank alcohol, it wasn't as if I was on heroin or anything silly. It wasn't like I was on heavy drugs!

Society in general is always getting on their high horse about other forms of drug addiction. People often call for life sentences for Heroin pushers, or Ecstasy dealers. I am not saying that this is wrong or condoning other drugs, but alcohol kills more people every year than Heroin, Crack, Cocaine, Speed, Ecstasy, in fact ALL other hard drugs COMBINED! Whereas 'hard' drugs kill about 1000 people per year in the U.K., alcohol kills over 40,000! Yes you read correctly, over **ONE HUNDRED PEOPLE A DAY** die because of alcohol in the UK alone. It is common to see people sitting there with a cigarette in one hand and a drink in the other saying *"look at the youth of today on all these drugs"*

Do you know the name Leah Betts? You probably do...she is the poor girl who died at the hands of the drug Ecstasy. Her picture was on huge billboards all over the country to highlight the dangers of that drug. Every television programme, radio programme and newspaper carried the story for months, some for years. There was an outcry from society calling for something to be done, to look at what the youth of today are on, and to try the person who sold her the drug for MURDER! In that case then perhaps our government along with the alcohol industry should be tried for murder for the deaths of FORTY THOUSAND people each year, after all, they are making the biggest share of the profit from this legalised drug pushing aren't they? It is difficult to calculate the exact number of people that are killed through alcohol. It would be virtually impossible to know the true figure. Many families have asked doctors to leave out alcohol as the cause of death on the death certificate when a loved one dies. There are so many people who are now being affected by alcohol in so many different ways. The effects include:– sexual crime, physical and mental abuse, unwanted pregnancies, violence, family break-ups, 8–14 million working days that are lost each year due to alcohol, the 75% of stabbings that are directly attributed to alcohol, suicides, murders, rapes, beatings, poverty and homelessness. I could fill a whole book with just the death and destruction caused by alcohol and that is without the mental and physical abuse which alcohol inflicts on its victims! But that is not what this book is all about and more importantly it would not help the alcohol addict to stop drinking. It might open their eyes a little more, but they would still suffer if they stopped. They would still feel *mentally* deprived if they stopped. Drinkers already know these facts and, like all drug addicts, choose to block them from their minds. The reason for mentioning some of these facts and figures is to illustrate to you once again that there is only one thing that keeps anybody addicted to alcohol, and that is F.E.A.R.

There is the fear that we will not be able to enjoy or cope with our lives without a drink. The fear that we will have to go through some awful trauma in order to break free, or perhaps the worse fear of all, the fear that we can NEVER break free. But where did these fears come from? Who or what created them? Are they part of our genetic make up, character, or personality? Are the fears there because we are weak willed people? NO NO NO, as I stated at the start of the book, it is the drug itself that creates the fear and all the brainwashing from birth perpetuates it. As I will repeatedly emphasise throughout this book, people are not so much hooked on the alcohol itself, but what they have been brainwashed to believe that it does for them. Think about it, the fears were not there before you started drinking were they?

Before you started drinking you could enjoy social gatherings without alcohol, you were perfectly happy without it. Now I am not saying that you were living a stress free life before you started drinking, in fact, the most stressful period of many people's lives tends to be early childhood and adolescence. But when you were stressed as a child your first thought wasn't to fix yourself a drink to calm you down after a hard day at the nursery was it? When you went to jelly and ice-cream parties you didn't need drink to enjoy yourself or to remove your inhibitions. In other words you were able to enjoy and cope with life without drinking alcohol. So why did you have that *first* drink?

The answer is simply because of all the pressure to have one. We end up believing all the nonsense about alcohol, all the advertising and brainwashing. The problem is that you really are not an adult until you try your first drink. Our friends are doing it, our family does it, our film and television heroes are doing it, so it is inevitable that eventually we are going to have our first alcoholic drink. Unlike smoking, or other drugs, we are not even told that alcohol is dangerous or addictive. Alcohol is the only drug which is known to kill seven hundred people a week in the U.K. alone and yet doesn't even have a warning on the label! We are even encouraged by our parents to take alcohol. If you ask a smoker "Would you encourage your children to smoke?" the answer is a clear "NO WAY". However, so strong is the brainwashing with alcohol that the same question to an alcohol addict may result in a less clear cut answer. Many parents give their children their first taste of alcohol before they have reached double figures. It is often a little glass of wine with a meal or a sip of beer from Dad's can. My Nan even bought me a hipflask with my initials carved in it for my sixteenth birthday! Alcohol is so much the 'norm' that it is a mystery how some people *don't* get hooked, not why they *do*. Is it any wonder that ninety percent of our population drinks alcohol?

Once we begin to realise that we are hooked on alcohol and that the physical addiction is easy to overcome, then why do we find it hard to quit? It's because we believe that we are making a genuine sacrifice and are actually 'giving up' something worth having. We feel mentally deprived when we stop. This feeling of deprivation is the real problem, because as I have already illustrated, even if you do not drink for years but believe that you have 'given up' a genuine pleasure, then the feeling of deprivation and misery will still be there for the rest of your life. That is why there are people still going to A.A. for years after they stop drinking alcohol, people who are still pining and moping for a drink. That is why they are taking one day at a time; it is because all these people still feel as though they are missing out. They still feel mentally deprived!

This is one of the major fears that people have of quitting alcohol. The fear they will always be deprived and always be missing out. The fear they will have to fight a desire every day for the rest of their lives. It is this kind of fear that keeps people hooked and prevents them from even making the attempt to stop, and who can blame them? Who wants to go through life fighting a desire to drink, or feeling miserable and deprived for the rest of their life?

The good news is that you won't. Once you understand fully why you drink and you begin to realise that alcohol does absolutely nothing for you, then for the first time in your life you will start to realise that you will be 'giving up' NOTHING and therefore you will not feel deprived when you stop. You will not have to fight a desire, you will simply be elated that you don't HAVE to do it ever again.

So what does alcohol genuinely do for you anyway....,why do people drink it?

It is possible to understand why we tried the first drink, because of all the brainwashing and pressure put on us to have it, but what makes people have the second, third, fourth and hundreds of thousands after that?

There are three main reasons why people drink alcohol. It's either for the *pleasure* (whatever the addict perceives that to be), because it's a *crutch* (stress reliever, relaxant etc) or because they believe that drinking has simply become a *habit*.

There are a few alcohol addicts who believe that the *only* reason for drinking is habit, however I would like to put this one to rest at the start. People do not drink alcohol simply because ......

5

It's A Habit

I must admit that I used to believe I was drinking certain drinks simply out of habit. Not all of them of course, some were for pleasure and some to help cope with stress, but I honestly thought that some of my drinking was due to habit. But who was I kidding? Habit! It is amazing some of the reasons we come up with to justify drinking. Did I really think that I left my house, went to the off-licence, came home, opened the bottle and drank it, all out of habit? I can understand that we all get into a routine or habit of doing certain things, but it's easy to break other routines. For example, we drive on the left-hand side of the road in this country, but when we go abroad we switch to the right with no real problem. Some heroin addicts fool themselves into believing that they are injecting themselves through sheer habit as well, even society talks about a heroin *habit!* But anybody on the outside can see that it is pure DRUG ADDICTION. If it was habit they could just inject themselves with an empty syringe. It would save them a fortune! If it was just a *habit* people could simply stop doing it. Do you believe that people who lose their home, family, self-respect, dignity, pride, self worth, and sometimes their lives because of alcohol do so because they couldn't break a *habit?* Of course not, they do so because it's a DRUG ADDICTION like any other, not a *habit.* If you still think that some people are drinking out of *habit,* why is it that people who haven't had a drink in years are still taking one day at a time? Are they still in the *habit* of drinking alcohol? Are they still in the *habit* of buying alcohol? No! When you go on holiday to a place you have never been, to a hotel you have never seen and a beach you have never been on, are you in the habit of drinking on that beach? At that time of the day? No! How long does it take to break this 'habit' anyway? Is this the only habit in the world that you are in permanent recovery from? Is it the only habit that is never truly broken? Or is a more likely explanation that these people who haven't touched a drop of alcohol in years and are still finding it hard to cope are simply feeling deprived and down because they still feel as though they are missing out on something pleasurable? That they are not like *normal* people but have a disease for which there is no known cure! The reality is that alcohol addiction is just that, an addiction, not a habit.

The problem with alcohol addiction is that most drinkers really have no idea that they are hooked. They honestly believe that they are drinking because they choose to and because they enjoy it. If they cannot think of a rational reason why they are drinking they will resort to justifications such as *habit.* We have told the same lies about alcohol for so long that we all end up believing them. I was constantly justifying why I drank, all drinkers do. We instinctively know that we shouldn't be doing it. We instinctively know that it is not normal to poison ourselves. We sense that we are miserable at times if we are not allowed to drink. We even have moments where we sense that we just might be hooked. So in order to rationalise why we drink, we have to build up all these rational reasons for not being able to enjoy ourselves without taking a drug first. And as you know if you tell a lie long enough and hard enough even the person who started the lie will end up believing it.

The heroin addict may think that they are getting high, but any outsider can clearly see that they are simply trying to end the lows caused by the drug. Over 90% of people aged sixteen and over drink alcohol in the UK. That means that 90% of people you meet also have to come up with rational reasons as to why they drink. If people collectively use the same reasons to justify drinking, then we are bound to end up believing them, even if they make no rational sense whatsoever. Everything that I believed alcohol did for me was an illusion. The illusions simply confirm what we have heard for years, so that we end up believing that alcohol provides a host of genuine benefits. But does it? One of the biggest illusions is that alcohol provides the drinker with a genuine pleasure. Exactly what pleasure is there in drinking alcohol? If it's a *genuine* pleasure then it can only come from either the taste, the thirst quenching or for the marvellous effect.

So let's remove the brainwashing a bit at a time. First of all let's get it clear that...

6

Taste Has Nothing To Do With It!

 Taste really has nothing to do with why people drink alcohol. I understand that many people believe that they love the taste of their favourite tipple, but this is not why people drink. I used to believe that I loved the taste of a dry white wine, a pint of beer or a southern comfort, but I now realise that I never did. In order to remove this part of the brainwashing let me ask you a question. How did your first alcoholic drink taste?

Be honest. There isn't a single person in the world who, when they were having their first alcoholic drink wasn't secretly thinking, *"what is this rubbish? I'd sooner have a fruit juice!"* There isn't a person alive who, when they had their first drink, didn't feel physically and mentally sick! The reason is because alcohol is a poison.

The irony is that the awful taste is part of what springs the alcohol trap. Our fears of getting hooked are immediately removed because we are convinced that adults drink this muck because they actually enjoy the taste of alcohol. But you *never* do. Now before you think I've now lost the plot and there's nothing nicer on the taste front than a cool glass of white wine or an ice cold beer – hear me out. Have you ever drunk an alcoholic drink that you didn't like the taste of? No? Think about it. Of course you have, everybody who drinks alcohol has on more than one occasion. When the pubs have closed and you go back to somebody's house for afters and they only have a drink that you normally don't like, do you stop drinking? I have left my house at three in the morning looking for an all night kebab house, and paid £15 for a bottle of wine, which tasted like sewer water. I have drunk spirits that if you put a match to them would light up an area the size of London, but I didn't like the taste! When you are holiday and can't get hold of your usual tipple, do you stop drinking? I have seen people drinking wine with dinner at such times and stating as they drank it that the taste was too sharp or bland. So why drink it then? People delude themselves into thinking that they drink alcohol for the taste, but do they? I love the taste of bananas, but if there are no bananas at a social gathering I don't feel deprived or get upset. If after eating bananas I woke up the next day and I felt as though I had just been run over by I truck, I wouldn't carry on eating them just for the taste! If somebody offered me a banana, which I didn't like the taste of, I wouldn't carry on eating it just because it's a banana! People say that certain drinks have an acquired taste. But what does an acquired taste really mean? It means that you didn't like it in the first place. If you liked it you wouldn't have to acquire a taste for it, you would like the taste from the start. The reality is that you don't even acquire a taste for alcohol, you simply build up an immunity and tolerance to the drug, and get over the foul taste in order to get the alcohol into your body with the least possible aggravation.

Smokers believe that they enjoy the taste of cigarettes, yet they never eat them. This just proves that if you tell yourself something for long enough you will end up believing it. What is alcohol anyway? If we get down to reality, it's simply fruit and vegetation that has gone off! It has fermented, which means it's off. It is the process of decay – it is rotten! That is why it tastes awful. Pure ethanol is a colourless liquid and powerful poison. All poisons taste awful, they are meant to so that we survive. 'Yes, but surely when mixed with other liquids, alcohol tastes good?' No, alcohol never tastes good. The whole object of the mixers is to try and cover up the foul taste of alcohol. The first drinks that we tend to have are drinks that have been flavoured with fruit that *hasn't* gone off! A Martini and **lemonade**, Pernod and **blackcurrant**, etc.

This has been proved in recent years by the development and launch of *Alcopops* in 1995 and the recent introduction of drinks like 'REEF'. Alcopops have a stronger alcohol content than normal strength beers and are the fastest growing new alcoholic drinks of all time. Their sales tripled during the first year on the market. Is this really a surprise? Of course not. They are bound to be successful, as they don't taste like alcohol, they taste like orange, lemonade, blackcurrant, apple etc. All children love fruit and hate alcohol. So the alcohol industry thought, how could we get even *more* people hooked on this stuff? The earlier we get them, the quicker we get them hooked and the more profit we make. *(They obviously weren't content with NINETY percent)*. I know, we will cover up the foul taste of the poison alcohol with fruit flavours that they instinctively like, give the drinks names that are 'cool'. Names like "Two Dogs" whose slogan 'It's the dog's' of course means 'it's the dog's bollocks!' What rebel teenager could refuse?

A report from *Alcohol Concern* states

'An established control on young people's drinking has been that youngsters find traditional alcoholic drinks <u>UNPALATABLE.</u> With alcoholic lemonade, cola, flavoured milk etc, this control has been removed'

I remember sitting down to Sunday dinner when I was eleven years old and being allowed to have a small glass of wine with the meal. What an adult I felt, what a psychological boost for a young man. I would sip it very slowly and literally shudder after every mouthful. I hated the taste of it, yet later on in life I could at times get through three bottles in a night! What had changed? Had the taste changed? No, the difference was that I was addicted to it and couldn't enjoy myself without it. I was justifying my intake by saying that I enjoyed the taste. I said it for so long I believed it.

There is so much brainwashing involved even with the taste of alcohol. On one side you have your own rational brain, which knows that the first alcoholic drink tasted revolting and on the other side, wine tasting connoisseurs that are telling us that the taste of certain wines are worth hundreds, sometimes thousands of pounds. Do you honestly believe that any bottle of wine is worth thousands of pounds? You may well think at this stage that I'm just a bit of an uncultured git, unable to tell the difference between quality and sewer water. But in my mind there is no such thing as a 'fine wine' any more than there is 'fine heroin'! It is just the way it is advertised in your mind. Why is the person who drinks beer, perceived differently to the person who spends thousands of pounds on a 'superior' wine? One reason and one reason alone – the brainwashing! The person on a park bench drinking their alcohol from a can and taking their nicotine from a roll up, is seen very differently to the person smoking a hundred pound cigar and drinking the 'finest' champagne. But why? They are both taking the same drugs aren't they? What is the difference between caviar and taramasalata? They are both fish eggs. It is the conditioning and brainwashing that's all.

There are many people who have managed to convince most of the planet that wines improve with maturity. What a belter of a marketing ploy, you never have to throw it away. You simply let it gather dust and charge even more, how blooming clever! The fact is that nobody can tell if it's gone off anyway, because it was off to start with! That is what made it wine to begin with. How can the taste possibly improve with age? Can you think of one other drink, or type of food, that if you left it alone for years, would taste better than when it was first produced?

There also seems to be a couple of contradictions to 'their' theory that gone off fruit and vegetation improves the older in gets. Have you heard of Nouveau Beaujolais? According to those in the know, you must drink this within 24 hours of being bottled. They say that if you don't you may as well pour it down the drain. I am just a tad confused here, one minute they tell us that the stuff improves with age the next it deteriorates with age? It's the same stuff, isn't it? I could be wrong, but it appears to me that the difference is simply in the brainwashing. Even Champagne, which is perhaps the most over rated sparkling wine in the world, has a 'use by' date on it!

The ways in which the tastes of alcoholic drinks are described are full of contradictions as well. For example, *'That's a tasty drop of bitter'*. How can anything that tastes bitter be called tasty? It's called bitter because it tastes bitter. Bitter means an unpalatable harsh taste, in other words not nice. Some people think they like the taste of sweet wine, but what they like is the sugar additive. Anyway the opposite of sweet is bitter, yet the opposite of sweet wine is *dry* wine. How can any liquid be DRY? Wines are described as flippant, cheeky, good nosed, precocious, sombre, and even mysterious! The only mystery is why we fall for the hype in the first place.

There are even wine tasting experts! There are even television programmes which promote wine tasting. And what do these wine 'experts' do with it once they have tasted it? They spit it out into a bucket! What did you want to do with your first alcoholic drink when you tasted it? Spit it out! But if we did that we wouldn't look like an adult. If I had known this at the time I would have spat it out and just told everyone that I wasn't being rude but I was a connoisseur and that they were all uncultured fools!

Do people have any idea how they appear tasting fruit that has gone off and been trapped in a bottle for YEARS to go off even more, then spitting it out into a bucket and proclaiming to the world that it has a 'full body'! Perhaps these people have done it for so long that they actually believe what they are doing is sophisticated and intelligent? I hear some people say "that wine has a lovely body to it" Now I have been drunk many times and I would occasionally get a good looking person mixed up with an attractively challenged one, but I would never think that a bottle had a good body! 'A good body?' 'A full body?' What??? There really are people educated way above their own intelligence aren't there?

If we saw children doing the same thing with different soft drinks, we would stop them immediately. Can you imagine seeing a group of children all taking mouthfuls of orange and apple juice, then spitting them out into a bucket and telling everyone that they were 'cheeky' or had a 'good nose'? We would want them sent to the nearest psychiatric ward. But if adults do it with fruit that has gone off, we give them their own television programme!

Have you ever sent back a bottle of wine at dinner? You know, when the waiter pours out the tiniest of drops for you to try and you sip it as everyone looks on with great anticipation? Very few people have, even if they are unsure to the taste of that wine and think it a bit sharp, they still nod and say yes. I know I have done many times. After all, we don't want to look uncultured or lacking in sophistication do we? What is all this nonsense anyway? Why do they only do it with wine? They never do it with the beer, the coke, the water, the meal, the dessert or anything else for that matter, so why do it with wine? Because it is part of the pretentious crap that keeps people hooked. As mentioned, if you say something for long enough you can end up believing it yourself. It all tastes like rubbish, because it is rubbish, literally!

If you persevere with *any* drink that contains alcohol, you will eventually get used to the foul taste. This creates the illusion that you enjoy the taste. The taste doesn't change just because you persist with it. The taste remains identical to the very first fix you had. Your brain and body has simply built up an immunity and tolerance to the taste. If you still think that taste has got something to do with why you are drinking alcohol, why not drink non-alcoholic drinks? There are now some on the market which **taste** exactly the same as 'normal' alcoholic drinks. But that just wouldn't be the same would it? I tried drinking non-alcoholic beers and wines on many occasions, but I just couldn't get used to them. The reason for this was that there was no *alcohol* in them. Heroin addicts could inject themselves without filling the syringe with heroin, but that wouldn't be the same either. Reason; no *heroin* in it!

There are many drinks out there that taste so much better than any alcoholic drink. I have always loved the taste of fruit juices. I have always found them much tastier than alcoholic drinks, *even* when I was drinking. However, I would always drink alcohol because taste had nothing to do with it. I wanted the alcohol. I felt a dependency and fruit juice just did not fill that dependency. And if you are still not convinced that taste has nothing to do with it try drinking pure alcohol! (On second thoughts don't, it will probably kill you!)

If taste had anything to do with it, nobody would ever take their second alcoholic drink. Whether they admit it or not, all drinkers feel instinctively stupid drinking. However, they can block this from their minds most of the time as the majority of people are doing the same thing. If you are doing something collectively, which goes against your rational judgement, you do not have to come up with any rational reasons to justify what you are doing. It is only when you are alone that you really start questioning it. Nobody likes to take any drug alone. I do not simply mean with nobody around, I mean the lone drinker in the company of people who are not drinking. This is one of the only times when people really question their drinking. This is when we instinctively start to know that what we are doing is stupid.

For years smoking was also seen in the same light. It was at one time seen as *abnormal* if you did not smoke. Smoking was never seen as drug addiction, and people had no idea that they were hooked. They have only started to sense that they are hooked since they have had to stand outside buildings in the freezing cold to get their fix. Smokers also say they like the *taste* of certain brands of cigarettes. Yet they don't eat them! And if they cannot get hold of that usual brand they will smoke any brand, even a brand they normally would never touch, simply to get hold of the nicotine. I deluded myself for years that I loved the taste of alcohol. Yet if I were on holiday and my usual tipple was not available, I would drink anything that contained alcohol. Even if it tasted disgusting!

Poisons in themselves can never taste good, they were never meant to, this is part of our survival mechanism. Alcohol however is a liquid and should, in theory, quench your thirst. Quenching your thirst is a genuine pleasure as I'm sure you'll agree. But this again is one of the many illusions which alcohol creates. Let me prove to you why alcohol is incapable of...

7
Quenching Your Thirst

Here is one of the cleverest aspects of this whole confidence trick. Alcohol is a diuretic, which means that it makes you pee. Have you ever noticed how you drink one beer but pee out THREE! This process dehydrates the body. You may know this already as you may have experienced the 'Sahara desert' syndrome. This is when you wake up during the night and find yourself trying to pour fifty gallons of water down your throat in a minute flat! You also notice that a French man has moved into your head and is pounding every inch of the inside of your skull. This is because your brain has shrunk! (Yes you read correctly, your brain is now smaller than it was the day before). The brain is mainly made up of water, as, indeed is the rest of the body. The more alcohol you take in, the more water you lose. It's a simple mathematical equation! What you are feeling is the pounding effect of blood trying to pump through a dehydrated brain. With water you only need one or two glasses to quench your thirst, but alcohol causes dehydration. That is why I managed to get through sixteen pints of lager a day, at one time. The more I drank, the more dehydrated I would get. The more dehydrated I would get, the thirstier I would become. The thirstier I got the more beer I would drink! And bear in mind that the alcohol content of the whole drink is usually very low. The rest of the drink is made up mainly of water. But even this additional water is still insufficient to cope with the diuretic quality of alcohol. Alcohol dehydrates so much that even with as little as 3% alcohol and 97% water, the 3% alcohol will not only use up the 97% water, but also rob the body of its own stores.

I'm not saying for a second that a pint of beer after a game of football, rugby, or a glass of wine at lunch time on a hot sunny day doesn't quench your thirst at all, but the alcohol in the beer or wine certainly didn't do it. You wouldn't drink neat alcohol to quench your thirst would you? Alcohol itself is incapable of quenching thirst, it actually causes you to feel thirsty. What a product, the people who make and sell alcohol are on to a winner. They are selling a liquid which causes you to feel thirsty, so that you buy more of the liquid to try and quench the thirst, which it created in the first place! Clever! It is the equivalent of walking around with heavy shopping *just* to get the relief of putting it down!

This is a subtle part of the pleasure trap. I will soon be explaining how alcohol is incapable of providing a *genuine* pleasure. However, when you have an aggravation, like thirst for example, then ending that aggravation is pleasurable. But would you deliberately cause yourself an aggravation to make it nice when you relieve it?

Again the drug is creating a low, but deceives its victims that the ending of that low is a genuine pleasure. I could not drink sixteen pints of water in one evening. That is because water is *genuinely* capable of quenching thirst but alcohol does the complete opposite. So part of the illusion of enjoyment is momentarily ending the aggravation of thirst that the previous drink had created. In the end, you would eventually need some water hence the 'Sahara desert' syndrome!

How on earth can anybody predict when they will be thirsty anyway? *"Want to meet on Friday for a drink, I just know I'll be thirsty at about 9pm!* ' There are billions of drinks out there that will quench your thirst, but alcohol isn't one of them.

So if it's not for the taste, and it's not to quench your thirst, then it must be for the ….

8

Marvellous And Pleasurable Effect

Ah yes, the marvellous and pleasurable effect of alcohol – that rather strange feeling that alcohol causes in the brain. But what is that strange feeling, is it a genuine pleasure and does it really make us feel truly happy and merry? Can we ever really explain or describe 'that feeling' anyway?

As previously mentioned, when you are doing something that you instinctively know to be stupid, you have to come up with any reasons you can to justify what you are doing – not only to other people, but also to yourself. And if you say it long enough, you end up believing it and will not question whether what you are saying makes any rational sense or not.

Heroin addicts believe that they enjoy injecting themselves with a powerful poison, which will zombify and stupify them. They believe that the destruction of their lives is the price they have to pay in order to get that marvellous pleasure. Alcohol addicts believe that they enjoy drinking a poison, which will zombify and stupify them. They believe that the destruction of their lives is the price they have to pay in order to get that marvellous pleasure. But the biggest illusion when it comes to alcohol is the illusion that it provides us with a genuine pleasure, that alcohol can make us feel happier.

I have said over and over again that I loved and enjoyed drinking. I honestly thought that I did at the time, but I now see clearly that I had simply fallen for a very clever trick. Alcohol fools you into thinking that you are getting true pleasure when you are not. Heroin addicts think they get a genuine pleasure when they plunge that needle into their arm and fill their vein with heroin. Yet all they are actually enjoying is the relief of trying to end the awful lows that the drug itself has created. The poor heroin addict is in a constant battle to end those lows. They are desperate to get back to the position that they were in before they started taking the drug. In fact the only reason why they continue to take heroin is to try and feel like a person who doesn't need to take heroin!

The only problem is that they are trying to gain control over something that is controlling them. The more they try and gain control the more they lose it, the more they lose it, the more they try even harder to gain it. The body will always build up an immunity and tolerance to any drug. So they need more and more to try and relieve the withdrawal pangs. The more of the drug they take the less it is actually going to relieve them, the less it relieves them the more of the drug they take. The more the drug drags them down the more they are fooled into believing that the momentary ending of the low caused by the drug is their last pleasure or crutch and the *more* dependent they feel upon it. They think if this is life with my crutch, then I do not want to face life without it. The sad truth is that they are not deriving any *genuine* pleasure from heroin and anybody who does not take the drug can easily see it. However, for those in the trap, they remain partially blind. They still believe that they cannot enjoy or cope with their lives *without* the heroin. They have a real fear of stopping and the drug is the very *cause* of that fear.

Many heroin addicts will often go back to the drug even after they have gone through the *withdrawal*. Some stop for years yet are still taking one day at a time. They are saying that they are never really free as they could go back at any time, but for *today* they are resisting it. The sad truth is that they are pining away for a pleasure that does not exist. They continue to feel mentally deprived because they believe they 'gave up' a pleasure. The bad side meant that they had to stop, but they still feel as though they are missing out.

The sad truth is that alcohol works in exactly the same way. This is why there are many people in the world who have stopped drinking but still feel a void. They are taking one day at a time trying to resist the marvellous pleasures of alcohol. The whole AA philosophy is staying sober for one day. Being strong and resisting temptation for one day. Take each day as it comes. The sad truth is that these people are also pining away for something that does not exist. They are going through mental deprivation for nothing. Whilst they still believe they have made a sacrifice, they will always feel a void to some degree. This confirms their belief that alcohol fills a void, but it is how they are *thinking* that is creating the void and the feeling of being incomplete.

The truth is that when you *stop* you actually return to normal. We never needed alcohol before we started drinking it. The need has only arisen since we started to take it. I remember going to parties as a child. I remember Christmas and birthdays as a child. I did not need alcohol to enjoy myself. I never had a fear that Christmas or my birthday would be a disaster without alcohol. I never thought that I would one day reach the stage where I would panic at just the thought of not being able to drink alcohol on my birthday. That just the thought of celebrating New Year without alcohol would scare the life out of me. That just contemplating the idea of going out at the weekend without drinking would make me feel miserable.

When I was a child I used to look forward to the weekend like all my friends, but not because it gave me the opportunity to drink as much alcohol as I wanted. It was because of the free time it gave me to live and enjoy life to the fullest, to go and play!

I never thought that I would become so lethargic and tired that my main source of pleasure would come from a bottle! I never thought that I would ever become dependent on a drug. That I would reach the stage where my confidence would be shattered so much that I wouldn't be able to stand at a social gathering and talk with my friends without having a drink of alcohol at the same time. I never thought when a child that I would ever end up like the adults I saw. When I used to see adults drinking I would think why? It smelt disgusting, tasted disgusting and made them stupid, tired, over emotional and aggressive. Why would anybody want to do that? It is a complete mystery to children why adults drink. Yet a few years after I had my first *fix* I would wonder how anybody *could* enjoy themselves or get true fulfilment *without* drinking alcohol, including children!

If you were at a children's birthday party do you honestly think that they would be genuinely happier if they had some alcohol inside them? When you see a child crying would you give them a drink to cheer them up? When you see a child laughing would you give them a drink so that they can get even happier than happy? When you see a hyperactive child do you think that by giving them alcohol they would become genuinely relaxed?

You wouldn't because you would know for certain that alcohol would not relax them or make them happy it would simply stupify them and mask the problem. Would they enjoy that stupified state? How could they? It would no longer be them! They are not feeling any genuine feelings any more as alcohol numbs all of the senses. They are no longer functioning properly. The magnificent machine that is the human body is now malfunctioning. When alcohol hits their brain it deprives them of their natural senses. It leaves them unprotected and vulnerable. If you gave a child alcohol on their birthday not only would they not get any genuine enjoyment but they would also miss that birthday. The alcohol would permanently deprive them of that experience, forever! How can you truly experience any emotion when you do not have access to your genuine feelings?

Children do not need alcohol to enjoy themselves so why do we feel the need? Why do we feel as though our lives would no longer be complete *without* alcohol? Why should we feel that something would be missing if we stopped doing it?

It is because *of* the alcohol itself that we have these feelings. The alcohol *creates* our fears. We were complete before we started taking alcohol, it is only the drug itself that creates the feeling of being incomplete. This means that alcohol addicts feel a constant void. They try and fill this void with the very thing that created it! Whilst they still believe that they are not complete without alcohol, they will never *feel* truly complete even if they stop.

From an outside view it is very easy to see that alcohol would not provide a child with a genuine pleasure. So why do we think the same product would work differently for us? It is because when you are in the alcohol trap yourself you become blind. Just like the heroin addict becomes blind to what they are doing. Your perception of what is really happening becomes distorted. The nature of drug addiction is to make the addict believe that the drug is doing the complete opposite to what it is actually doing.

For example, alcohol dehydrates the body but appears to quench thirst. So part of the illusion of pleasure is the ending of thirst. But as mentioned it doesn't end it, it caused it in the first place!

Alcohol is a depressant but appears to cheer people up. However, it only appears this way to the person 'under the influence' – not to a sober person. It is only the perception of the person drinking alcohol that has been changed not anybody that they come into contact with.

I know that when I was sober and I tried talking to someone who was drunk, the last thing I wanted was to feel like they did. I could see that they were not genuinely happy. They were in a *stupified* state. I could not communicate with them, it was not even worth talking to them because I could see clearly that it was not them. But I was fooled into believing that this is what drink does to *them*. I was convinced that it never did that to me. After all I felt better when I had a drink, or so I was led to believe. Once drink enters the brain your perception changes. You feel a *false* sense of pleasure and control and you believe at times that you are happier. If you are with other addicts it appears normal. Everybody is experiencing the same feeling. But what is this 'feeling' anyway? And do we ever really enjoy it? What true pleasure do we get from an alcoholic drink? If we had to sell it could we do it?

I remember my first experience of getting drunk. I was about ten years old and I drank some wine. The feeling was awful. The room was spinning, I felt sick and I was sick, literally. I felt completely out of control and dizzy. The next day I felt as though I had been run over by a steamroller. I never enjoyed it for one second. So did the feeling change as I got older? No the drug is *never* different, just my perception along with the many lies I voiced to deceive myself. The only difference was that my body had built up an immunity and tolerance to the drug, so it took a lot more alcohol for me to reach that state. So the first few drinks at lunch time were just topping up the low feeling created by the previous drinks I had consumed. As you will no doubt be aware when you first start drinking, one drink floors you, now it takes slightly more to do that. The alcohol has not changed only your body's tolerance to the poison. Some people build up such a tolerance to the drug that even while they are drinking, they still feel the need for a drink. The more they drink the greater the need. The greater the need the more they drink. So in their desperate bid to escape they sink to the bottom of the sand even faster. All to try and get back to how they felt before they started drinking. Another fact that most alcohol addicts are not aware of is that it can take 72 to 240 hours for your body to get over physical effects of alcohol. In other words the low caused by the drug. Some people describe this as *withdrawal*. This is usually imperceptible to the alcohol addict most of the time, they are used to feeling this low and regard it as normal. If they have more than their tolerance level, they will become more aware of the low – hangover. Their body then builds up more of a tolerance to the drug every time they exceed their usual tolerance level. After a while they believe that the ending of the low is a true high. Which is the same as putting on a pair of ski boots, wearing them for a couple of days, just so that you can get the pleasure of taking them off again!

Alcohol is a double-edged sword when it comes to creating the illusion. One is the partial ending of the physical low, the other is that it's mind altering. Alcohol addicts believe that this is where the pleasure really lies, but does it? We say that we drink to get 'that feeling'. But what is that feeling?

The feeling I thought I was enjoying is a short circuit in the brain – literally! People sometimes describe 'the feeling' as a feeling of being 'light headed' and they say that they enjoy feeling 'light headed'. But isn't that the same as feeling dizzy? People sometimes say that they like feeling dizzy. Well turn around then, it will save you a fortune! I never drank alcohol to make me feel dizzy, I drank it for the same reasons that heroin addicts inject themselves with heroin – because I felt as though I could not enjoy or cope with my life without my drug! I never *consciously* thought this as I believed that I was getting a *genuine* pleasure from alcohol and that I was *choosing* to drink.

But I was never really *choosing* to drink and I was never getting a *genuine* pleasure.

Some argue that people laugh more when they're on alcohol. In some cases this is true, but when I was seven years old living in Halifax (north England) I was hanging around a bunch of similar aged kids who always had a smile on their face due to GLUE SNIFFING! Is this a good reason to sniff glue? Is it genuine happiness they are feeling? Does their inane smiling mean that glue sniffers are genuinely happier than those who don't sniff glue? Of course not!

YOU ARE NEVER REALLY YOU!

Alcohol removes your natural fears and you become unprotected and vulnerable. The part that controls our rational and intellectual thinking has been removed, we become literally *stupified* when alcohol takes effect. This state is also known as inebriation.

This is good, I hear you cry, it is good to let your hair down once in a while and act a bit silly. I agree and I do frequently. You do not need alcohol to do that, just look at children! At least when children do it, it is actually *them* doing it so they can get the genuine pleasure of letting their hair down and acting a bit silly.

And it would be fine if we could actually genuinely enjoy that stupified state, but I believe that the biggest downside to being addicted to alcohol is that you are never really you. If you are taking the drug you are not fully you, there is a part missing, you are incomplete, so you are not you. And if you are not allowed to have some, you feel uptight and miserable so you are still not you.

Alcohol takes away your natural senses. So any feeling that you have when under the influence is all *false*. If we step outside of the trap for a second and take a real look we can see clearly that alcohol does not genuinely make people happy and merry and that there is no genuine pleasure to be had from drinking alcohol.

Alcohol is a **depressant!** The longer you take a depressant the more depressed you become. This is an undisputed medical fact. If alcohol made people happy, then doctors would prescribe it on the N.H.S. as an *anti* **depressant**. If alcohol made people genuinely happy, then whenever they were really down and lonely, they could just sit in doors, drink a couple of bottles of wine, or better still, a bottle of scotch, and be as happy as pie again. In fact if you did that you would be even more depressed, because alcohol is a **DEPRESSANT!** (If you are still in doubt then ask yourself why over 65% of suicide attempts are alcohol related!) If alcohol made you happy and merry why would you want to end it all? Surely when you are happy, the last thing you want to do is commit suicide.

Am I suggesting for one second that I have never been happy at the same time as having a drink? NO, of course not. I was bound to be happy at the same time as drinking on occasions, it's the law of average. Nelson Mandela was happy at times when he was locked up in prison for twenty-seven years. Not because he was locked up, but in spite of the fact! I was happy at times when I was drinking not because of the drink, in spite of it! Really open your mind on this one and realise that it is NEVER the drink that is making you happy. The alcohol never changes it is always the same, it is only the occasions where you take it and the people you are with.

When people are at funerals it doesn't matter how much they drink, they still feel sad. This is because it is a sad occasion. When people are at an exciting party with fun people, they will be happy. This is because it is a happy occasion. Or they should be happy at a good party. However, the sad truth was if I was at a party and I *couldn't* drink for whatever reason, I would still be miserable. It wasn't that I was happy with alcohol, but miserable if I could not have it. I would say "parties are just not the same when you are not drinking". But I only felt this way because I was like a child having a mini mental tantrum, I felt as though I was missing out. I also felt almost naked at these times without a drink. I felt as though I could not enjoy myself in the same way without my drinking partner – alcohol!

Yet the alcohol never provided any genuine pleasure or enjoyment and it certainly never made a party. Although I used to be convinced that it did. After all the party is always better when everybody has had a few drinks, isn't it?

Well, answer this question if you will. Have you ever been to a really lousy party? Have you ever been to one of those dos that were as boring as hell with dull and miserable people? If you haven't I'd be very surprised. Everyone has been to a party that was just a complete waste of time. Let me ask you another question, was there alcohol at this party? Were you drinking alcohol at this time? The answer is, of course, yes. I went to plenty of terrible parties and still do. I believe that people continue going to parties in the hope that they just might be as good as the half a dozen parties they can recall enjoying! The fact is that if alcohol as a product made people happy, outrageous, and fun people, then all you would need to ensure a party's success would be to make absolutely certain that everyone was drinking alcohol.

Equally, you will have probably been to several parties where you have been drinking and had a great time. So it's obvious that it's not the alcohol that determines whether you have a good evening, but the company, the banter, and the sociable aspect of being out with good friends, the music and the dancing, but **never** the alcohol.

Certain drinks will *appear* nicer than others, but the alcohol never changes only the situations where you drink it. The drinks that appear the nicest are taken at times when we should be enjoying ourselves anyway. They are drunk at the nicest *times*! The ones when we're having a meal with friends. The ones at lunchtime and after work. The drinks when we are having a nice relaxing bath. The ones when we are on holiday and at parties. In other words times when we should be relaxed, calm and enjoying ourselves anyway. After all, these are all happy occasions anyway aren't they? But why do we feel as though we cannot enjoy ourselves without alcohol? I used to always say that I could easily enjoy myself without alcohol and I would come up with at least two references where I did not drink and was OK. This was a way to justify why I was drinking. To show others and myself that it was not out of dependency, but choice. The truth is that the drinker is not *choosing* to drink at these social times, they *have* to otherwise they feel a void and miserable. The fact that the addict does not realise that the drug *created* the void is neither here nor there. The addict believes that it fills the void. But if people really had a *choice* would they want to get drunk?

Answer this question: Each time you have had a drink can you honestly say that you have been happy and merry at the same time? Have you ever been uptight or argumentative whilst drinking? Have you ever been stressed out whilst still drinking?

Have you ever felt depressed or cried whilst still drinking? Have you ever become obnoxious or unreasonable whilst still drinking?

Think about it. If you have experienced any of these emotions at the same time as having a drink then it should be blatantly obvious that alcohol does not make you happy and merry. You drink on occasions where you should be happy anyway and the alcohol has got some of the credit. You also drink at times when you feel down and the situation is then to blame, not the alcohol. In theory every time you drink alcohol you should be laughing and enjoying yourself, but you cannot say that is what happens **every time** you drink alcohol can you? If alcohol as a substance genuinely makes you happy and merry, then wouldn't you agree that it should work every time you drink it? For example; if you are thirsty then you know for certain that water will definitely one hundred per cent quench your thirst and solve that problem. But does alcohol make you feel happy every time you drink it? The answer is a clear and resounding NO!

I bought into the idea that I could drown my sorrows with alcohol, after all alcohol makes people happy doesn't it? So when you are feeling down it should perk you up. The reality is the opposite, if you drink alcohol whilst you feel depressed, you will feel even more depressed than you were feeling to start with. Do people look happy and merry when they are smashing bottles into people's faces after drinking? Do people look happy and merry when they are being obnoxious, argumentative, aggressive, abusive, violent, loud and hurtful towards people when they have been drinking?

But Jason, this is what can happen if you have *too much*, but a little alcohol does make you happy and merry.

Hang on! Too much alcohol and these things can happen but having a little makes you happy and merry? Who are we kidding? If alcohol makes you happy then surely the more you have, the happier you should feel, not the opposite! What is this *"a little alcohol is OK"* anyway? It is a drug and as such you are compelled to have more. Once you start drinking you have no real choice. You either continue drinking more and more, or, you will have to exercise a degree of willpower, discipline and control not to increase your intake. One of the biggest gains from being free is to not *have* to use willpower, discipline or control over my alcohol intake.

Someone recently asked me if I stopped drinking because I *couldn't* control my intake any longer. I stopped because I did not *want* to control my intake any longer. It is a constant battle when you have to use a degree of willpower and discipline to try and keep in control. As I mentioned, it is the exercising of control which means that you are not in fact in control. It is so nice to be free!

The only reason why having a little alcohol appears to create happiness for some people is because it removes your natural fears and satisfies your psychological dependency for the drug. The truth is that you should be happy anyway at social gatherings. I will explain why the removal of your natural fears (caused by this short circuit in the brain) creates all of the illusions in the following chapters. However, the point is that you are in a position now where you cannot be happy at certain times without alcohol. You should feel happy when you are out with friends anyway, but as a drinker you are only happy if you have a drink at the same time. And if we are honest isn't that really true? You can continue telling yourself and the listening public that you enjoy a drink, but can you take it or leave it? Are you in control of your drinking or is the alcohol, either consciously or sub-consciously, controlling you? I will tell you now that every single person who drinks alcohol on a regular basis is *not* in control. I asked you at the start of this book to have an open mind so that you can see what is really happening. Alcohol addicts feel dependent, but most alcohol addicts are fooled into thinking that they are not dependent but drink out of genuine choice.

I went through most of my drinking life thinking exactly the same thing. We may believe that we are drinking because we choose to, but can we be sure that it is not because we *have* to? We thought that it was our choice to have the first alcoholic drink, but the reality is that we were conditioned to have it and pressured to have it. The choice was never really ours to begin with. So how do we know that it is our choice now to continue to drink? It's not always easy to know. So lets help clear the confusion with a simple and straightforward question. I have asked the following question to many alcohol addicts some, with very little money and self worth:-

'If I said to you that you could have a lottery win of one hundred thousand pounds, would you take it?

Of course everybody answers yes to that question. However in order to keep the money there is just one tiny set back – **YOU CAN _NEVER_ DRINK ALCOHOL _EVER_ AGAIN.** What would you say? Would you have to think before making your decision? What decision would you make if you were honest with yourself? Would you take the money?

I know what I would have said when I was hooked…stuff the money! What would be the point of all that money if you couldn't enjoy yourself? What would be the point in all that money if you could *never* have a drink again? Think of the vacations you could have with all that money, but what would be the point if you could not have a drink by the poolside? You could have a great party to celebrate your win, but what would be the point? It would hardly be a party without alcohol. Sod the money, let's have a drink!

That is the same answer I get eventually from every alcohol addict that I have asked. At first many said that they would take the money. I thought, surely not if you're honest. Then I realised that most were not being honest. That is after all the nature of drug addiction, to try and prove that you are not dependent and in control. All drug addicts lie including drinkers, not only to other people, but also to themselves. Telling me that they would take the money is a nice way to convince themselves and myself that they are in control and not dependent. Because it's a hypothetical question, they can say anything and they know that they cannot be proved wrong. But when I really questioned them and asked would it really not bother you that you could never drink ever again? They said *"Well if I am honest, not only would it bother me but you are right, I wouldn't do it. There is more to life than money you know"*. There is also more to life than alcohol, but the addict does not see that. It really reveals the true reason why people drink, the massive fear of stopping drinking forever. If someone said to me, here is one hundred thousand pounds, and said that I could keep it provided that I never eat another banana. I would say stuff the banana! I happen to love bananas and they are important for a healthy diet, but I wouldn't even have to think about it.

The reality is it's not that alcohol makes you happy, it's that you are miserable without it now. You have drunk alcohol at every social gathering for years, so you simply cannot *imagine* what life would be like without it. Your only reference to what social gatherings are like without alcohol, is when you are *forced* not to do it. It may have been because you were driving, on medication, being nagged, "on the wagon" or whatever. So your brain now says that a night without alcohol makes you unhappy, and a night with alcohol makes you happy. But the alcohol is not what is making you happy, it's just that you felt mentally deprived when you couldn't have it, so you were miserable without it. This is because you have always relied on alcohol to help you to enjoy every social gathering. The only reason that you feel the need is because alcohol has created that need. In the following chapters I will illustrate how alcohol destroys your courage. Before you started drinking you relied on *you* and you were more than happy to do that. As I have illustrated, you could enjoy the highs without alcohol and handle the lows without the drug, before you started drinking. Of course we have the usual fears, inhibitions, apprehensions and inexperience which all children have. But we quickly overcome those fears and inhibitions as children. If you do not remember, look at children's parties. The children walk in with the usual fears and inhibitions, but within five minutes they have destroyed the place. They do not need alcohol, heroin, crack, cocaine or any other drug, they are already on a high, a *natural* high, feeling great just to be alive. They are already in that position and the frame of mind that the alcohol addict is trying to achieve by drinking alcohol. The addict will never achieve this fully as the drug *caused* them to feel incomplete in the first place. The irony is that they could so easily get to the same position if they did *not* drink alcohol! It causes the very problem they are trying to solve.

The challenge is that most alcohol addicts do not believe that they are drinking to end a low, they think it's for the pleasure. But when you see children at a party what pleasure exactly are they missing out on? The wonderful sensation of being drunk? The marvellous pleasure that we are all apparently enjoy? Where is this marvellous and pleasurable effect anyway?

Is it the pleasure of not being able to communicate properly? Is it the marvellous effect of losing all of your senses so that you become immediately vulnerable and completely unprotected to all dangers around you? Is it the wonderful feeling of becoming totally stupefied? Is it the marvellous effect of not being able to focus or walk properly? Is it the pleasurable effect of talking complete and utter rubbish for hours on end? Is it the pleasurable effect of vomiting? Is it the pleasure of blowing your mind so much that you become a completely different person? Is it the marvellous effect of destroying your memory so that you don't even remember your apparently wonderful experience anyway? Is it the marvellous and pleasurable effect of losing all the check points between your brain and mouth so that you get loud, aggressive, obnoxious, foul mouthed, nasty, hurtful, uptight, annoying, repetitive, pathetic, over emotional or abusive? Is it the marvellous effect of being *out of control*? Is it the wonderful effect of not being able to make love or show true love and affection because you are too 'out of it'? Is it the pleasure of saying and doing things that you will regret for many years to come? Is it the marvellous effect of feeling dizzy?

WHERE IS THIS MARVELLOUS EFFECT? It doesn't exist, it's one huge fallacy.

When you see people who are drunk, when you haven't had a drink yourself, does it really make you want to have some alcohol so that you can get the effect that they are apparently *'enjoying'?* When you see someone during the day for example who is drinking from a can of beer in the middle of the street, do you envy them? Not many alcohol addicts do, but why not? Don't you want to have fun too? Don't you want to feel happy and merry all the time? Don't you want to get that marvellous and pleasurable effect?

Alcohol can never make an evening or improve a vacation, it has certainly destroyed a few. The alcohol gets the credit when it has nothing to do with the alcohol.

I went to Tunisia a few years ago, when I was still drinking. The first few nights were spent in the hotel bar, where they had some really "stunning" acts for our entertainment. Personally I think a better time would have been had painting a door and watching it dry! Still, we were in the middle of nowhere and there didn't seem to be anywhere else to go. I was, of course, drinking every night. This makes me sound like a heavy drinker, but every alcohol addict when on holiday drinks virtually every night. This is because they have no restrictions preventing them from taking their drug and they feel as though they cannot enjoy themselves without it. The point is that although I was drinking the evenings were very, very, very boring, and if there is nothing to stimulate your mind when you are drinking you get very tired very quickly. I was only there for a week and on the fifth day we decided to go on one of those pre-arranged evenings with a meal, entertainment and free wine all night. It was the last part that appealed so strongly to me at the time! The evening was excellent, the best evening of the whole week and made the holiday that much better. Was the evening so good because I was drinking? NO, I had been drinking every night before that evening! It was because the atmosphere was excellent. There was belly dancing, snake charmers, a room filled with about five hundred people all clapping and dancing on the tables and on the big stage in the middle of the room. I was dancing and interacting with people and it was a really fun evening. This had *nothing* to do with the alcohol. I had an excellent evening, not because I was drinking alcohol, but *in spite* of the fact I was drinking alcohol.

If somebody had said to me at the time that there wouldn't be any drink, the sad truth is that I would have rather stayed in the hotel bar drinking, than attending this event without any alcohol. I was convinced at the time that some of the success of the night was due to the amount I drank. Looking back I didn't actually drink that much at all during the evening. I was too busy dancing and having fun.

In fact, I have been to several social gatherings when I was hooked, where I had an excellent evening and had hardly anything to drink.

And haven't you? Have you ever been to a social gathering where you were perhaps dancing all night and had very little to drink? At the end of the evening you realise that you have had an excellent time and yet you hardly touched a drop. To your surprise you could have even brought the car and driven home. But if you were told that you **couldn't** drink then you would have felt miserable and deprived. The truth is that we do not need alcohol to enjoy ourselves, because alcohol does not make you enjoy yourself, it is a depressant. We just think it makes us happy because we feel miserable if we can't have it.

UNDER THE INFLUENCE

The biggest danger of the alcohol trap is that it gives the addict an illusion of control. This sounds like a contradiction, especially when you see someone who has taken alcohol when you haven't, but alcohol removes natural fears and inhibitions. When that happens you feel as though you are more in control, but you are not. This leaves the person out of genuine control. They immediately become vulnerable and unprotected. When you are driving your car, you have to be alert and slightly un-relaxed in order to make sure you don't injure yourself or other people. It is natural to have some fear at these times, it's this fear which is vital for our survival. However, when alcohol short circuits the brain it removes this fear and gives the illusion to the addict that they are calmer, therefore more in control, and happier. The addict's perception has now changed and they feel as though alcohol has provided them with a genuine benefit. There are still some people who believe that they are better drivers when they have had a couple of drinks. I used to be one of them. Was I stupid for thinking this? No, the reality is that I *did* feel calmer, more relaxed, and in control at the time, but these were illusions. But how was I to know when I was the one who was literally under the influence? When I woke up the next morning my perception of what had happened had not changed. I felt hungover and I thought I had been outrageously stupid to drink and drive, but I was still led to believe that the feelings I had when I was 'under the influence' were real. They say that a good friend should never let you drink and drive. That is true and a good friend wouldn't. A friend that actually knows what they are doing that is. It is no good asking a friend to hang on to your keys so that you don't drive home if you have too much to drink. Once they are 'under the influence' it is not them any more. Your true friend has already left and the someone who remains just wants to get home. You may drive to a pub with all the best intentions in the world, but as soon as that alcohol short circuits your brain, you feel a false sense of control. _You_ would never drink and drive, but it's no longer _you_ who is driving home! "Under the influence" means literally that, being controlled in what you say, do, and think.

People often say that the truth comes out when you are drunk. RUBBISH. What comes out is far from the truth. I have said and done things that I would NEVER have dreamed of doing when "under the influence"

Most people, however, realise that people on alcohol do not drive better but are in fact endangering the lives of others as alcohol slows down their normal reactions. This realisation is mainly due to M.A.D.D (Mothers Against Drunk Drivers). Their campaign in the early eighties led to people changing their whole perception of drinking and driving. But it still wasn't enough to make me ask myself that if alcohol gave me control, but was in reality taking it away, were all the other reasons I gave for drinking fallacies too? Like the fact that it makes you happy and merry and a fun person. Alcohol does not turn you into a fun person. How many people do you know that are dull people, annoying people, when they have a drink they don't turn into fun people do they? Far from it, they become even more annoying and even duller and all you want to do is get rid of them!

In truth, alcohol does none of the things which we are convinced it does. Including the one about ....

9
It Helps Me To Relax

In what situation does alcohol help us to relax? I used to find the drinks that helped me to relax were consumed when I was in what should have been relaxing situations anyway. We must keep this point very clear, the alcohol never changes. Circumstances change, situations are different, but never the alcohol.

I would come home from work, fix myself a drink put my feet up and think, "ah that's relaxing" But coming home from work and putting your feet up is a relaxing time anyway. It is a way to unwind from the pressures of the day. Most of the time I would take just one mouthful of the drink and I would think that it was the drink that was helping me to relax. It didn't even occur to me that the alcohol hadn't had time to take any effect! The truth is that your brain will do as you tell it. If you tell your brain that you cannot relax without a drink then the brain will say "OK, I won't relax until you get one then". That is why I could relax after just one sip. But the drink was not genuinely helping me to relax, it was a *relaxing situation.*

In reality, the only reason for being so unrelaxed was partly due to my alcohol addiction. Alcohol does create withdrawal. However, unlike heroin where the withdrawal is very noticeable, with alcohol it is very subtle. Now anybody who has reached DT stage is no doubt at this point disagreeing. *"What about the terrible physical withdrawal that is 'delirium tremens'?"* Do we mean the shakes? Are we talking about not being able to hold a cup properly because our hands are shaking too much? The body trembling? I would like to ask you a question "do these people look *relaxed* when they are trembling and shaking?" It sounds like a ridiculous question, but it is simply to illustrate a point clearly. When someone is shaking, trembling and ill at ease they are clearly *not* relaxed. What <u>caused</u> this feeling? THE ALCOHOL ITSELF! Nothing else caused this feeling, only the alcohol. The addict then has some more alcohol and the shakes stop. The drinker now has the belief that alcohol helped them to relax. The reason is because they *are* more relaxed than they were a minute ago, but nowhere near as relaxed as they would feel as a non-drinker. This is because even whilst they are drinking alcohol they are still only *partially* suppressing the un-relaxed feeling that the alcohol caused. The more of the drug they take, the more withdrawal they will have, the more withdrawal, the more of the drug they take to try and stop it. They have treated the symptom of the disease with the very cause! Until they remove the cause they will *always* suffer with the symptoms because they will always have the disease.

Even though nearly every drinker has at least once suffered from the shakes (the morning after feeling when you have had just *one* too many), most of the time they are not aware that the body is in an almost permanent state of recovery. When the body is getting over the physical and mental pounding of having poison flood the bloodstream, it becomes *unrelaxed*. For the body to *fully* recover from this below par feeling, it will take anything from three to ten days. The average alcohol addict very rarely goes longer than four days without a fix. In order to see how part of the illusion works we need to understand exactly what happens when alcohol enters the body.

Alcohol goes straight through the stomach wall without being digested, giving an instant rush of glucose to the bloodstream. This will stimulate the excess production of the powerful hormone – insulin. Any rush that you feel when you have alcohol is simply the rush of insulin going through your blood trying to burn all the alcohol you have just put in. The insulin produced to deal with this actually causes your blood sugar levels to fall. Yes *fall*! When you feel the effects of low blood sugar what do you need? A quick fix! The moment the insulin reaction has cleansed your bloodstream of this excess sugar, you are then running on empty. When you feel empty you feel unrelaxed, but when you have more alcohol you instantly feel more relaxed because you have loaded your bloodstream with glucose and have momentarily suppressed that empty feeling. But again, all that has actually happened is that you have partially ended a low that the drug itself caused. A low that, for most of the time to the average alcohol addict, is imperceptible. Now I see how this accounts for the really low feeling on a Sunday morning after an alcohol binge on a Saturday. I would always crave a big fry up and now I know why, I was suffering from hypoglycaemia – low blood sugar. This accounts for why many alcohol addicts eat a lot of sugary foods and why they are running on *nervous* energy!

So alcohol causes low blood sugar, drains the body of water, over works the liver, pancreas and kidneys, and takes oxygen from the brain. Doesn't sound very relaxing to me!

The truth is that alcohol does not help anybody to genuinely relax. We tend to fix ourselves a drink at relaxing times. A lunch break, finishing work, having a long hot bath, after doing the chores, a dinner party, lying on a beach, or having a meal. The drink gets the credit, but alcohol is incapable of giving genuine relaxation. If you drink alcohol in situations that are not relaxing, will the drug create the feeling of relaxation you are craving?

In truth, all the reasons for drinking are illusions. The same people who say that alcohol helps you to relax will also tell you that alcohol livens up any social gathering. If you tell me that a product calms you down, I might believe you, but tell me that the same product livens people up, and I have to question your sanity. What drug can do the complete opposite of what it did half an hour earlier? People drink for the opposite reasons that they drank the day before;

"I got the pay rise, let's celebrate by having by having a drink" or "I did not get the pay rise, let's drown our sorrows by having a drink"

THE DRUG NEVER CHANGES ONLY THE EXCUSES WE GIVE TO JUSTIFY OUR INTAKE!

Did we start drinking to help us relax? Did our parents encourage us to drink alcohol before we took our exams so that we would feel calm and relaxed? They should have in theory. Come to think of it we should all be encouraging children to have alcohol before they go into exams. That way they can feel calm, relaxed, confident, courageous and happy whilst tackling this unnerving task! If people honestly believed that alcohol genuinely relaxed them, then why do bosses get so annoyed when their staff have had too many at lunch time? Surely it is good to have a calm and relaxed work force, isn't it?

If we believed our own hype about alcohol, let alone everybody else's, it would make sense to take drink all the time. When you wake with worries on your mind, why not have a drink to relax you first thing? It would seem the logical thing to do if you believed that is what alcohol *genuinely* does for you. If you see a person being violent, the first thing you should do is give them a drink to relax them. Can you imagine a country where over 90% of the population were taking a drug on a regular basis that helped keep them calm and relaxed? Wow, you would simply have little or no crime in such a society. It would be the calmest and most laid back nation in the world. We can but dream of such a place!

The president of the United States should be advised to drink alcohol constantly. To be a world leader, he should be confident, courageous, relaxed, strong and dominant wherever possible. Boris Yeltsin *always* looks the picture of happiness and courage doesn't he? He always looks a very calm and relaxed individual, don't you think? Relaxed! He can barely stand up because of alcohol! This is not relaxation, it is being drunk, and there is a *big* difference. He can hardly run a bath let alone a country!

You are *never* genuinely relaxed when drinking alcohol. When a heroin addict is lying on some floorboards do they look relaxed or totally 'out of it'? When you see an alcohol addict collapsed in a heap on the floor do they look genuinely relaxed or 'out of it'? "Out of it" means just that, out of, or void of *any* genuine emotion or feeling.

People often try to argue that alcohol is an anaesthetic. This is true, but being anaesthetised does not mean genuine relaxation. Heroin is also an anaesthetic, in reality a more powerful one than alcohol, but would you take heroin to help you to relax? And would it genuinely relax you anyway? Do you believe that a heroin addict is more relaxed than a non-heroin addict? If you were having a nice relaxing jacuzzi with a person who has just taken some heroin who would be more relaxed? And who would be tired and zombified?

We *need* access to *all* of our senses at a moments notice. If we are relaxing and a door slams, we jump. We are meant to jump, who knows what danger there might be. Someone relaxing on alcohol will often be unaware of the danger.

When a powerful poison like alcohol enters the blood stream, the body has one of two options. It can either store it, or get rid of it. Alcohol is so poisonous to the human body that it cannot be stored for very long or you would die. This is why all the alcohol leaves your body within the first week to ten days. The body has no choice but to get rid of it. Alcohol is removed by the liver at a rate of one unit per hour, this process cannot be speeded up by drinking coffee, or anything else for that matter, (again that is another fallacy). This process takes up so much of the energy in your body that your muscles, bones, in fact everything feels tired, or RELAXED as we have been conditioned to say. But the reality is that your body is a long way from *genuine* relaxation, your body is extremely unrelaxed because it is getting a pounding from a poison! If you pass out on alcohol it means that your body cannot keep you alive and awake at the same time! The body needs all its resources to deal with the poison in the bloodstream. When you lose the use of your sight, hearing and consciousness you are effectively in a coma! Being comatose is not relaxation.

The addict, however, remains blind. I certainly did. In order to want to feel relaxed you must be unrelaxed to begin with. Why are alcohol addicts so tense? I couldn't relax properly even at a social gathering if for some reason I wasn't allowed to drink or I had to control my intake more than usual. There is nothing more unrelaxing than being a slave to a drug. The mental and physical slavery never really occurs to us.

Of course I was tense and found life tough. I was permanently below par both mentally and physically because I was dependent on a drug. I used to get snappy with people at times when I had a drink and also when I couldn't have one! If I was drinking I was 'under the influence' and if I couldn't drink I was 'under the influence'. I would feel mentally deprived and that would make me unrelaxed. Just like a child being told that they cannot have a toy and kicking up a tantrum. When you see a child having a tantrum they are mentally unrelaxed because they are being denied something they want. It is exactly the same as when a drinker cannot have a drink when they want one, or more importantly *need* one to cope or enjoy themselves.

"Give them a drink to steady their nerves"

We hear that all the time, yet alcohol destroys the central nervous system. The only nerves that alcohol can steady is the nerves of somebody who is already suffering from the *withdrawal* effects of alcohol! Even then it only suppresses them temporarily because it *caused* them! When you see a person smashing a broken glass into someone's face in a pub would you ever even for a second think "I know what they need to steady their nerves – another drink?" When somebody is shouting obscenities when they have had a drink you would never think "give them a drink to calm them down!" Why not? If you believed alcohol to be a genuine relaxant? Give them enough alcohol and they will eventually pass out, but again that is not true relaxation.

Alcohol has even found its way into outer space. The Russian Mir space station is apparently partly fuelled by vodka! Not the station itself but the Russian cosmonauts on board. American astronauts arriving for duty on board the Russian craft were said to be amazed and flabbergasted to be offered a stiff drink of vodka to calm their nerves after a tricky spacewalk. It is said that one particular Russian spent his time aboard Mir completely out of his head. (Or totally spaced out!) Why didn't they have a drink *before* the space walk so that they could feel relaxed *during* this tricky task? Because they would be dead by now if they had done!

It can be concluded that alcohol does not help to genuinely relax at all and that this feeling is another fallacy. I also mentioned in this chapter that alcohol destroys your courage and confidence, *surely* I am not suggesting that alcohol does not give people a little bit of good old ......

10

Dutch Courage

'YOU CANNOT BE COURAGEOUS WITHOUT OVERCOMING FEAR'

Not only am I suggesting that alcohol does not give any genuine courage or confidence, but I am categorically stating that it does the complete opposite. Alcohol destroys your courage and confidence and this is the most detrimental part of the whole confidence trick. One of the biggest gains of being free is having true confidence and courage back again.

When you see somebody of 3ft nothing and built like Kate Moss taking on Arnold Schwarzeneger after they have had a drink, does anybody think for one second that they are being genuinely courageous? No, everybody thinks they are being stupid, not courageous. However, the addict believes that the feeling is genuine. Alcohol removes our natural fears so that we feel a *false* sense of confidence and courage. If you do not have any fear then you simply *cannot* be courageous. A courageous act can only happen where there is fear to overcome. How can you have any genuine courage if you don't feel fear? Are we ever really fooled away? When you see uncle Tom having a go at the waiter after having a drink, do you look back in admiration and say " I never realised that Tom was such a confident man" or do you apologise profusely and say "please ignore Tom, it's just the drink talking?"

The truth is that the person on the outside is never fooled, however Tom, (the addict) is. Even when Tom wakes up he is still fooled into believing that how he felt the night before was genuine. So an easy way for Tom to obtain confidence and courage is to drink alcohol again. But the problem is that it is all false. Some people ask does it actually matter if the feeling is false, if the addict believes it to be real then there is no harm in it. Yes there is! There is tremendous harm in removing your natural fears to give yourself a false sense of courage and confidence for two very important reasons:

When we remove our natural fears we become unprotected and vulnerable to all kinds of dangers. We technically negate the most powerful survival mechanism we have. There is a drug out at the moment commonly referred to as the 'date rape' drug. This drug puts the intended victim into a zombified state so that they do not know what they are doing or where they are. All of their senses get numbed and their natural fears, which are there to protect under such circumstances, are removed. Sound familiar? We need our natural protective fears, without them we put ourselves in the position of being both deaf and blind to all dangers around us. Sight, hearing, smell, taste, touch and instinct are all there for a good reason, to help us live. Remove them and we literally become helpless!

Two teenagers who are about to fight may feel brave but at the same time they are probably hoping that someone will stop the fight before it's started. Even if the fight goes ahead, usually the second that one of them goes down, the other will stop and is considered the 'winner'. The worse that tends to happen is a bloody nose or two.

However, give them alcohol and you remove their natural protective fears of getting hurt, hurting others or the consequences. The only time you see somebody getting kicked repeatedly in the face, even when they are unconscious and have blood pouring out of them, is when people are *low* on drugs. The most horrendous violence is usually drink related. The people doing the kicking are not being courageous, as their natural fears have been removed and the person lying on the floor would probably not have got involved in the first place, had they been able to fully judge the situation.

Imagine a herd of antelope being stalked by a lion. The antelope have no choice, it is not a case of fight or flight, only one of flight! All the antelope are on edge and nervous. They are meant to be. This is not a bad thing, it is very good! But if one of the antelope had alcohol in its system then their judgement would change, their reactions would be slower and they would lose their fear. They would then have no reason to use their flight mechanism. Are they being brave? No. Their judgement has simply changed and they are now rendered disabled, vulnerable and unprotected. And that is what happens when we take alcohol, we become disabled, vulnerable and unprotected. We become blasé to any danger around us and at the same time we believe that it is genuine courage. When a young girl is walking back from a night club by herself she is *meant* to be slightly nervous and on edge, to a certain degree. Anything could be around the next corner and she needs her wits about her. Alcohol removes those fears and replaces them with a false sense of confidence. At times like these you do not want confidence, false or otherwise, you *need* your natural fears.

The second, and I believe the most detrimental problem with this false sense of courage, is that the addict actually *believes* it is real. All the time alcohol is actually depressing the central nervous system and doing the opposite to what the addict believes. So whilst the addict is 'under the influence' not only is the alcohol not giving them any genuine courage or confidence, but it is preventing them from using their own. This will suppress their true courage and confidence so much that in the end they will be convinced that they are just not a confident person. They end up convinced that they cannot live *without* the drug!

Why Look For Something When You Don't Think You Have It?

In the film *The Wizard Of Oz*, the lion had lost his 'C-c- courage'. At the end of the film he found it again. The truth is that he always had his courage. He never lost it at all he just hadn't used it for a long time. The longer he went without using it the more he was convinced that he had no courage. That made him more and more fearful, thus confirming his belief. How did he find his courage in the end? By having a drink of alcohol? No of course not! Do you think that there is one person in a million who saw the film and thought the lion could obtain genuine courage by drinking alcohol? NO! He found his courage the very second he *used it*! The very second he felt fearful and broke through those fears. If he had taken alcohol he would have been given a very false sense of confidence and would *never* have found his genuine courage. Why look for something when you *believe* that you have already found it? (think about it).

The alcohol addict believes strongly that alcohol helps to *give* them confidence and courage, but it's an illusion. The longer they believe it, the more fearful they get that they cannot live without the drug. I used to believe that you had to be a really confident person to live without alcohol. But why did I think something as ridiculous as that? I never thought I was being confident or courageous for *not* taking heroin in order to enjoy or cope with my life. I never thought for one second that *not* taking crack-cocaine made me more confident. I never thought that I was a confident person because I was living without the need for LSD! But to the person who is dependent on these drugs they strongly believe that life would never be the same again without the drug. They believe that those who do not take the drug are just confident people who do not *need* anything. They blame their personality or genetic makeup when it's the drug itself that is suppressing their true identity. As I will repeat over and over again throughout this book the drug causes the need for the drug. I felt as though I did not have the courage to do something as simple as stop drinking alcohol. The fact is that I always had my courage but just like the lion I hadn't used it for a while. What was stopping me from using it? Fear. Fear that the drug itself had caused. The longer I took the drug the more fearful I became that I couldn't enjoy or cope with my life without my drug. The more fearful I became the more alcohol I would take to overcome those fears. But it's always the alcohol that CAUSES THE FEAR!

How can something that creates fear give you courage or confidence?

I reached the stage where I thought I didn't have the courage or confidence to enjoy a football match, a birthday, a meal out, or New Year's Eve without a drink. I loved all of those occasions before I stated drinking and I wasn't fearful of them. Why? Because there is nothing to fear about those situations there is only something to look forward to with excitement and anticipation. Alcohol creates this damn illusion that you cannot live without it and yet it is *only* the alcohol that makes us think that way. We never thought that way *before* we became hooked.

Children have fears too, but they break through them using their genuine courage. Look at children at birthday parties, they sing, dance, play and they don't care about making a fool of themselves because they are living and having fun! Alcohol addicts are even fearful of doing that. They believe that in order to do that you need a drink first. Every time you overcome a fear you grow as a human, if you are not growing you are dying, there is no in between. This, I believe, is the saddest part about alcohol addiction. The more you depend on alcohol the more you are convinced that you cannot cope or enjoy yourself without it and the quicker you die inside. The less fulfilling your life will become. The less fulfilling your life, the more you rely on alcohol to fill that gap. This is why I was so fearful of stopping, I always thought that there would have been a permanent gap in my life if didn't drink alcohol. It is alcohol that creates the gap and getting rid of alcohol fills it. Now that the gap has been filled just the thought of drinking alcohol again puts fear into me, not the other way around. Why should we fear *not drinking?* That should be the real question!

Just like in *The Wizard of Oz*, I felt I was under a spell cast by the wicked witch. My life was being controlled and yet I thought I was in charge. The second I realised that alcohol did the complete opposite to what I was conned into believing the spell was broken. All I had to do then was let the wicked witch die. How easy was it to do this? By simply letting her starve to death. I was the person keeping her alive by feeding her the life force she thrived on – alcohol. This was the substance that she fooled me into thinking was helping me through the stresses and strains of life. She was masquerading as a friend! A clever con, but now I can sing "Ding dong the witch is dead. The wicked witch is dead" Do I miss her?

THERE IS NOTHING TO MISS!

Besides, what confidence do you need to do something that you have no control over anyway? You can only be confident when you are aware of your faculties and in control. Confidence means being *IN* control, so how can you be confident when you are *out* of control on a drug? It is never GENUINE courage or confidence when alcohol is in your system, it is *all* false! And once again the worst part is that you are not really you.

Alcohol destroys your courage and confidence. What confidence or courage do you need to eat a meal with friends? What courage do you need to lie on a beach, enjoy a party, or talk with people you already know well? Why should you ever feel *insecure* at these times? Exactly what confidence is needed to watch the football, go to a wedding, a christening, or even wake up in some cases! There are people who have already reached the bottom of this trap, 'skid row' as it is commonly known. These people cannot even function without a drink in the morning. Do you think that the drink is helping to give them the courage to get through another day? Or has the drug itself covered up their true confidence so much that they now believe it only exists in the form of a bottle?

"But I would never reach that stage because I am not an alcoholic" there is no such thing. You are in quicksand, you are in the confidence trick. Your confidence will not improve with alcohol it will slowly wither away as it has been doing for years. This will happen gradually and slowly so that you do not notice. This process is often so gradual that you will put it down to all kinds of other things – your job, family, lifestyle etc. I reached the stage where I couldn't go to any social gathering or cope with any stress without having a drink. I was just like any alcohol addict, my true confidence had been suppressed. I just didn't know how to enjoy myself at social gatherings without a drink. All I knew was that I was miserable without a drink at such

times and happier with one. I foolishly concluded that I was happy because I was drinking! But that was never the case. I see it all very clearly now, as I go out more now than I ever have done and I have more confidence now than I have ever had in my entire adult life.

I used to delude myself that I didn't *need* to drink. I believed that I was in full control of my intake, that I could take it or leave it. Yet I was aware that I *had* to control my intake, I had to permanently watch my intake, or at times worry about my intake. This is not control this is slavery, this is dependency! When you are dependent on anything it slowly destroys who you are. It wears you down. It drags you down. This is where alcohol really destroys your courage and confidence. Trying to keep control of something that is actually controlling you is extremely soul destroying. Especially when you believe that you are the only one having to do this. After all everybody else is telling you that they are in control, that they drink because they choose to, that they might drink a little too much on occasions but it's not like there is a problem. But what are you telling everybody else? You are telling them that you are in control, that you drink because you choose to, that you might drink a little too much at times but it's not like there is a problem! But that is the biggest problem. It is the permanent battle to try and keep in control of something that is controlling you. It is very easy to tell if somebody is not really in control, it is when they tell you that they *are* in control. Sounds like a contradiction, but let me explain. The fact that people think it's a major achievement if they haven't had a drink in a week and brag about it to everyone who is willing to listen, means that they are out of control. Why do people congratulate each other who have managed to stay 'on the wagon' for a couple of weeks? Especially when they say they get a genuine pleasure from alcohol and are apparently in control! What is so clever about stopping something for a week that you claim you are in control of? If they were in control why even brag about it? And why do other alcohol addicts congratulate themselves because they have been without their *pleasure* or *crutch* for a couple of weeks? It just doesn't add up. If I went a week without a drink I used to tell everybody. You hear it all the time, drinkers are always trying to justify how little they take and yet brag about how they can drink anyone under the table! If you are happy and proud of yourself because you have managed to go a week, or whatever, without alcohol, then the drug is controlling you. There are people who go on the wagon to prove that they are not hooked! As I mentioned at the start of this book, there is even a book on the market at the moment called '*How To Give Up Drinking For A Month*'. The author states that you should stop for a month every year to prove that you are in control. He also states that it will be very hard to do this and you will miss alcohol all the time. Oh and talking of time, he suggests a day by day planner so that you know what day you are on! So by stopping drinking for a month, counting the days and missing it all the time, this would apparently confirm that you *do not* have a problem with alcohol! But wouldn't this simply confirm your worse fears, that you do have a problem and that you are *not* in control? What does that do to your genuine confidence? Like everything to do with this trap, it shatters it. Think about that for a moment. If you were in control you would never need to buy a book like that in the first place, you would just stop doing it. If I wanted to stop eating bananas and I went around telling everyone who will listen that I haven't had a banana in week and at the same time I was reading a book called 'How To Stop Eating Bananas For A Month', wouldn't you immediately know that I had a real problem with bananas? Not only that, but you would make absolutely certain that I seek help immediately.

"*No thanks I'm driving*", "*I can't tonight I have work the next morning*", "*Not for now, I'm on the wagon for a couple of days*", "*just the one, I have a very important business meeting this afternoon*" I could go on, but the point is that all of these statements are proof that drinkers are permanently having to exercise a degree of willpower, discipline and control for their entire drinking lives. They always *have* to control and that is where it really drags you down.

As the drug suppresses your confidence more and more, the ability you may have to exercise this control between drinks gets reduced and reduced. Like all drug addiction the more it drags you down the more you will be fooled into believing that it's your last pleasure, or last crutch and the MORE dependent you will feel upon it.

But, as I have stated, the whole process of stopping drinking is easy and enjoyable. However, the fears of stopping drinking forever and the belief that you will be missing out for the rest of your life, cause people to feel stressed even at the thought of stopping. After all fear in itself is a stressful emotion. This is why people who stop even for just a couple weeks get very uptight and stressed, it's not the physical withdrawal from the drug, but that they feel as though they are missing out. The problem is made worse because the alcohol addicts have taught themselves and have been brainwashed by society to believe that alcohol relieves stress. So the more deprived they feel, the more stressed they will become, the more stressed they become, the more they will pine for a drink. Yet it is only the mental pining for a drink that is causing the stress! The irony is that, contrary to what you have been brainwashed to believe, and what you might think at the moment, alcohol is incapable of relieving a genuine..

11

Stress

I have said that if you tell a lie long enough and hard enough even the person telling the lie will end up believing it. This is exactly what has happened with the statement that alcohol *relieves* stress. Alcohol is the major **cause** of stress in the alcohol addict's life. Alcohol might block your mind to some of your stress, but genuinely relieve it – *never!* When the drug has worn off you still have the stress to deal with. It doesn't just go away because you block your mind to it. We, as intelligent human beings, tend to laugh at the ostrich putting its head in the sand, thinking that the danger has gone because it can no longer see it. But by thinking that alcohol relieves stress we are doing exactly the same thing. Every time you wake up after drinking, you are physically, mentally, emotionally, socially and financially worse off than had you not taken the drug. So you will be *more* stressed at this point. The genuine stresses you had the day before seem much worse than they actually were and now you are convinced that your life is very stressful. You never really put it down to the drink, but if you are permanently trying to get over the physical and mental effects of a poisonous drug like alcohol, then you will always have an additional stress. Just the physical effects of alcohol take at least **three days** to get over. Alcohol addicts think that if they have had a 'skinful' on a

Saturday night and a couple on the Sunday then they are fine by Monday morning. However, this is simply a level that they are used to. This is *their* normality. They honestly believe that this is a normal way to wake up on a Monday morning. They will simply put it down to the job, the children, the genuine stresses and strains of life, the fact that the weekend is over, but part of the stress is always caused by the alcohol they have consumed.

There is only one stress that an alcoholic drink is even *partially* capable of relieving and that is the stress caused by the last drink! But even then it doesn't do that. Some alcohol addicts near the bottom of the quicksand think *"at least it ends my stress of needing a drink"*. Does it? Or did it create that stress as well? I can recall numerous occasions when I was going to have just *one* drink and ended up having two, three, four, or however many it took until there was no more, or until I collapsed, whichever came sooner. Was I happy in this state? Was I calm? Was I stress free? I don't know because *I* wasn't there to enjoy it. All of my senses were numb, I was in a stupefied state. Whilst you are in this state, you remain vulnerable, unprotected, and with your head in the sand. And yet people take the drug because they believe that they are more courageous, more confident, calmer, relaxed, happier and stress free when taking it.

But alcohol *never* relieves stress it does the opposite.

Have you ever felt stressed at the same time as having a drink? Have you ever been uptight or argumentative whilst 'under the spell'? Ever got aggressive, obnoxious or loud when inebriated? Have you taken things out of all proportion, or just been plain rude, spiteful, or hurtful when drinking? I really don't need to ask these questions, I know you have and you know you have. *Everyone* who has drunk alcohol has experienced some, if not all, of these emotions when inebriated. If you have been stressed at the same time as drinking alcohol why do we believe that it relieves stress? Because just like the heroin addict, we feel better momentarily when we first get our fix. This is because we have ended the mental 'wanting' a drink created by the belief that it will help in *this* situation, while at the same time partially suppressing the physical low created by the drug itself. Mainly, however it is just one of the many excuses we use to justify our intake of the drug.

Either offender or victim has been drinking alcohol in 65% of murders and 75% of stabbings in the U.K. Do you think these people were stress free? Do you think *"it's a good job they had alcohol in their system to relieve some of their stress, otherwise God knows how many people they would have killed without it!"* Of course you don't, you know that these crimes were largely because of the (depressant) alcohol.

I was always more stressed when I was an alcohol addict than I ever am now. I was either on the drug, thinking about when I could take the drug again, trying to control my intake of the drug or coming off the drug. Non drinkers just do not have these stresses. I don't have them anymore. I used to get stressed whenever I heard the bell for 'TIME PLEASE' in the pub. I could have already had five pints and still one in front of me, yet I still wanted more, why? Was I stressed? Was I unhappy? Was I not being sociable? Was I unrelaxed? Did I need courage? Did I need confidence? NO, NO, NO, NO...... I just needed more of my drug like any other drug addict! I felt a chemical reaction that simply made me want more and more. I would sometimes walk to the ends of the earth to get more. I would pay any amount of money for 'take outs', money is never an issue when you have been chemically and mentally programmed that you *need* a drug. That is why, no matter how much it costs, when you are 'under', you don't care. This is also the time when you can clearly see that it's drug addiction, for, at these times you would drink sewer water provided it contained alcohol!

If the engine blows up in your car, you can consume a thousand alcoholic drinks, but you need a MECHANIC! If your partner leaves you all the drinks in the world will not bring them back or help you find another one. In reality it does the opposite. Hence *"I have never gone to bed with an ugly person, but I have woken up with a few"*. Alcohol really does change your perception!

Alcohol is incapable of relieving a genuine stress. It actually causes stress. Just ask yourself with an open and honest mind "how can a *depressant* solve *stress*? The only way to solve a problem is to deal with the problem. But how can you deal effectively with any problem when you are 'out of it' on alcohol? A good night's sleep will not solve stress either, but at least you wake up feeling refreshed mentally and physically so you are better equipped to deal with it.

Alcohol causes financial stress, physical stress, mental stress, and emotional stress. Exactly how does it relieve stress? Waking up and worrying about what you have said and done the night before. Worrying about how you got home or how you can face them? Or:-
"I really didn't mean to do it", *"God I wish I hadn't had so much to drink, I have a very important day ahead"*, *"How long will a taxi be, I'm freezing standing here at 2am in the middle of nowhere"*, *"I wish I wasn't drunk"* , *"I'd better not drive this morning, I think I am still over the limit"*, *"How much did I spend last night, where has all my money gone?"*, *"How did I get here?"*, *"Who are you?"* *"I feel like shit, I wish I didn't"*.

People who do not drink plainly and simply do not have these stresses. It is only the people who do drink who have them. Alcohol creates these stresses. When I was stressed, and still an addict I would normally say "God I need a drink!" I would then phone a friend to either join me at home for a bottle or go to a pub. As the evening progressed I would start to feel better. Why? Was it because the alcohol helped to put things into perspective? Or was it because I was able to talk about my stress with a friend? When you put anything into perspective you will feel less stressed. Alcohol *falsely* changes your perspective. When you wake up, you still feel stressed about the problem plus the additional stress of the *low* created by the drug.

But again the addicts themselves remain blind. To them it was the alcohol which helped, not the friend. However, the biggest stress is *having* to constantly *control* your intake. I now do not have the stress of worrying what day it is to see if I can take my drug without worry. I do not have to wonder how much I am drinking or how it is affecting my life. I do not have the stress of wondering when is the next time I can drink without *having* to exercise control over my intake, or the stress of *having* to hold it at just a couple because of work or whatever. I do not have the stress of feeling resentment towards others because I have to drive! I do not have the physical, financial, mental or emotional stress that feeling dependent on alcohol creates.

But once again, children provide the best example. If your child was stressed because they had too much homework or they were being bullied at school, would alcohol help their stress? So why do you think that it would help yours? For the same reasons that I did. It *appears* to help at times. Any outsider can clearly see that alcohol, far from relieving stress, causes it. Alcohol causes both physical and mental aggravation, which in turn *creates* various degrees of stress. Any form of aggravation, whether physical or mental will affect your ability to focus or concentrate properly. But there are some drinkers who believe the illusion that a drink *helps* them to .....

12

Concentrate

This is yet another clever con trick. Any form of concentration takes *mental* and *physical* focus. If you have an aggravation, like physically feeling the effects of coming off a drug, or feeling the mental dependency that you *need* one, then you will not be able to concentrate as well as you would without these aggravations. If somebody is suffering from the DT's (delirium tremens) they feel as though they cannot concentrate without a drink Again the truth is, the only reason that they cannot concentrate is because of the drink! In order to concentrate on anything at all you must first get rid of anything that is aggravating you. A heroin addict cannot concentrate properly without their drug, when they take the drug they are calmer and more relaxed thus better able to concentrate. But is there one non heroin addict in the world who believes that heroin helps people to concentrate? When I was 'on the wagon' for three months I couldn't concentrate properly at any social gathering. Even though the physical aggravation had gone, I still had the permanent mental aggravation of *wanting* to drink but not being able to.

Some people have built up such an immunity and tolerance to the drug that the withdrawal effects have become *normal* to them. They believe this is how they are meant to feel. The chemical reaction automatically sends a signal to the brain and the *thought* "I want a drink" occurs. Whilst they retain that thought then they will not be able to concentrate properly until they get what they want. Part of their focus has now been taken up with an urge caused by a subtle chemical reaction in the body. As soon as they fix themselves a drink they will be better able to concentrate. The funny thing is that as soon as they take a sip they will crack on with whatever they need to focus on, yet the drink has had no time to take effect whatsoever. It's psychosomatic! If the alcohol *did* take effect then they would definitely *not* be able to concentrate on anything. You need total concentration and focus to pass your driving test, why not have a drink before the test? Because it changes your judgement, slows down your reactions and causes mental and physical aggravation. Do you think that Tim Henman would concentrate better on his game if he had a drink in him before a big match? Would children focus better on their homework if they fixed themselves a little 'Scotty' (Scotch) before they began? A brain surgeon really needs a steady hand and full concentration to do their job – alcohol to the rescue once more! What an amazing drug alcohol is, it does everything! Sorry, it *appears* to do everything.

The only reason why alcohol addicts are better able to concentrate at certain times when they do have a drink is because they are either partially ending a physical low (caused by the drug) or they have satisfied their psychological dependency for the drug. The truth is that they are only ending an aggravation. When you eliminate any aggravation you are better able to concentrate than a moment before. But you shouldn't have the aggravation in the first place. Alcohol addicts are just aggravated without their drug at certain times, which is identical to a child being told they are not allowed to have a toy. Think about it logically, how can a depressant that destroys brain cells, numbs all of your senses, (including sight, which is a valuable aid to focus!) slows down your reactions, and stupefies you, help you to concentrate? It can't! It is just another con.

But Jason, if you have nothing to do and you are kicking your heels then at least alcohol helps to relieve ....

13
Boredom

I've said that when we are doing something that we instinctively know is stupid, we have to come up with some rational reasons to try and justify it. However, this particular excuse really takes the biscuit!. In my private sessions I often get drinkers telling me that alcohol helps when they are bored. Help what? The boredom? Alcohol cannot in any way help to relieve boredom. In order to succeed we have to be honest with ourselves. If you are sitting indoors by yourself and bored out of your head, if you have a drink in your hand you are still bored! When I was a child and I was bored, my Mother would never say "Oh, have drink son" she would say "Go and do something". Why did that always work? Alcohol is a drug and as such CREATES a void, when you have a void in your life you can feel bored a lot of the time. The effects of the body trying to repair itself after you have taken the drug, and the gradual suppression of the nervous system can also lead to boredom. After all, every minor task can appear a mountain to climb when you feel as if you have just been run over by a truck! You can reach a permanent stage of tiredness and lethargy, so often you just can't be bothered to do anything. If you have enough alcohol it will knock you out so I guess you are no longer bored, but then you are no longer anything. Shooting yourself in the head would also knock you out and it would solve your boredom for life! The only way that alcohol can relieve boredom is when you watch somebody who is drunk, you're not bored then because you know *anything* can happen! Alcohol is incapable of relieving boredom, once again it helps to create it.

If we look closely at some of the apparent rational reasons that are given to justify our alcohol intake, not only does alcohol fail to do what we think, but it does the opposite! Most of the *reasons* we give contradict one another anyway.

'IT CALMS ME DOWN' and 'IT LIVENS ME UP' Two complete opposites!

How can the same drug help to solve a completely opposite problem, from one minute to the next? It can't, it is just part of one of the cleverest con tricks ever devised.

The truth is that alcohol does the opposite to what it *appears* to do. It causes mental and physical stress, mental and physical tension, mental and physical aggravation. It suppresses your nervous system, destroys your courage, undermines your confidence and keeps you a slave.

Yes Jason, but I do not drink to help to relieve stress or to help with my boredom I am just a social drinker and you cannot escape from the fact that even if alcohol doesn't do anything else it is a tried and tested ....

14

Social Pastime

 I can easily dispute the "fact" that alcohol is sociable, because it is far from a fact. I suppose you could say that it is a social *pastime* if you change the meaning slightly. A lot of "social time" will literally *pass* you by, when you are a slave to alcohol. To refer to alcohol as a ***pass-time*** would be correct according to this definition. Just think of all the happy evenings, the nights out, the weddings, christenings, parties, the intelligent conversation, the dancing, games, banter, and the days you have **MISSED** because of alcohol. I am not talking about the time you missed where you were physically present, but your mind was blown, but the time you miss because you have to exercise willpower, discipline and control because of the drug. I would, on many occasions, choose not to go out and be sociable if I knew I had an important task the following day. I knew that if I went out I would end up drinking more than I wanted to, which I didn't want, or that I would feel deprived all night because I wasn't drinking, which would be equally bad. So I would often stay in and be unsociable because of alcohol.

During the four years that Paul Merson was not drinking, according to an article I read, he became very unsociable. He apparently would be the first to say that he stayed in most of the time watching telly. He felt as though he couldn't go out without having drink. The main problem with alcohol is that you are never *you* at a social gathering, whether you are drinking or not. If you have to restrict your drinking because you are driving for example, then you will not be yourself; you will feel miserable and deprived, because you cannot have a drink. However, if you are allowed to drink then you won't be yourself either. This is because it numbs your senses. In order to feel any genuine emotion you need your senses. Alcohol also slurs your speech, which if I am not mistaken, is an extremely valuable aid to being sociable. The drug also takes away all reason and common sense. It makes you overemotional, loud, and sometimes spiteful and hurtful. It can turn you into an obnoxious, annoying, and argumentative person *(which is very sociable!)* Alcohol stupefies you, but more importantly, it removes those very important check points between your brain and your mouth. You know the check points I'm talking about. Those which check your thoughts and stop certain ones turning into speech. This is for your own protection and everybody else's. Alcohol removes those very vital check points. Consequently no matter what comes into your head, no matter how obnoxious, rude, offensive, or stupid, it ends up coming out of your mouth. You often end up talking complete and utter nonsense for hours on end! That is, of course, if the anaesthetic effects of the drug haven't caused you to pass out altogether *(Which may sometimes be a relief to all around!)* Being passed out is a wonderful **pass**time!

I went to a lovely New Year's Eve Party last year, a black tie do, with some very close and dear friends. Everything was set for a good sociable evening, good company, good food, great atmosphere, great music *and* a good reason for celebration – New Year. There was also FREE champagne available all night. (When I say free, I mean *financially* free, as there is always a price to pay for drinking alcohol) The first part of the evening was taken up with people asking why I didn't drink. I will cover this later as it warrants a chapter of its own. The drug alcohol (or champagne as it was specifically named that evening) helped to destroy the rest of the party for many people, and many people unsurprisingly became very *unsociable* because of the alcohol. One person I know had his head slumped on top of the bar for most of the evening and was actually asleep before Big Ben had chance to chime for the New Year. What exactly is sociable about that?

Others were fine for the first couple of hours; they were talking, laughing, interacting and being sociable. I was also being sociable, being social means interacting with others. The reason most alcohol addicts are seemingly fine for the first hour or two is because our bodies are very clever survival machines. As we continue to drink alcohol week after week, our bodies think there is no choice but to take this poison. They will automatically build up an immunity and tolerance to the poison so that we survive. This means that we need more and more to get the same effect or illusion. This again is why our first ever alcoholic drink floored us and we now need a lot more than that to get the same result. The more of the drug we take, the more the body builds up an immunity to it, the larger the immunity and tolerance, and the more of the drug is needed to achieve the same illusionary effect.

So, at first, everybody was fine and actually being sociable. But again I must emphasise, the fact that they were drinking did not make them sociable. What made them sociable was being at the party and talking to people, people who do not drink are also very sociable at these times! I was also being sociable but I *wasn't* drinking alcohol. This continued for a little while, however, as soon as the alcohol started to really kick in, the inevitable started. It started off with:–
"I f_ _ king love you!" then *"I f_ _king love you bastard!"* then it just turned into *"YOU BASTARD!"* What was meant to be the best party of the year turned into an occasion where people became argumentative, aggressive, obnoxious or spiteful. Other people present became very over emotional, tearful, or jealous. There were people falling over, collapsing on the floor, bar and tables. Others were literally being sick. The ones who managed to stay upright continued to talk rubbish, or danced (well kind of) and were not aware of the evening they experienced anyway. They, personally, were not there. They, personally, missed out on one of maybe only 80 or 90 New Year's Eves they will ever get the chance to experience in their lives! When asked the following day if they had had a good time, many stated *"I must have, I can't remember a thing!"* If you can't remember the evening, how on earth do you know if you had a good time? How can you be sociable if you can't remember what you were saying or doing?

The reality is that they *were* being sociable until the alcohol took effect, as soon as it did, they became unsociable. I was one of the only ones left standing at four o'clock in the morning and I still wanted to dance, I still wanted to be sociable, but there was no one left to socialise with. WHY? Because of the alcohol. It is so obvious when you can see it from an objective point of view. I was convinced for years that alcohol helped people socialise, especially when they were meeting for the first time at a social gathering. I thought, "top up their drinks as often as possible to get everybody talking and get over that awkward period". But, in reality, this doesn't work, there is still that awkward period and people do not interact just because they have had a drink. If you are shy and inhibited, then alcohol will not solve that problem any more than an ostrich putting its head in the sand will remove the danger. I have been to parties and social gatherings in the past where I have been drinking alcohol, but still stood in the same place all night talking to a small group of people that I already knew! Surely that is frequently the case? At social gatherings we tend to talk and interact with people we already know. Sometimes we talk to other people, at a dinner party for example, (when you are inevitably stuck next to Mr and Mrs Dull) but on the whole we usually interact and socialise with the people we are comfortable with and already know. Would I have been unsociable if I had been drinking something other than alcohol?

Of course I wouldn't. If I was stuck at home moping away because I was on the wagon or feeling miserable at a social gathering because I *couldn't* drink for some reason then, yes, I <u>would</u> be acting unsociably. But again, it would have been the alcohol that caused these problems anyway, people who do not feel the need to drink do not have these problems. If you do not feel mentally deprived, you will happily socialise no matter what is going into your mouth! There are non-drinkers who are very dull and boring people, but then there are drinkers who are also dull and boring people. There will always be dull and boring people, that is part of life, but alcohol won't help these people to socialise, it will eventually have the opposite effect. It will ensure that people become loud, idiotic, abusive, and all the other possible symptoms that go along with drinking alcohol, which will guarantee that they end up even less popular than they were to start with!

All drug addiction appears sociable...*to the addict that is*.

There is a park in Switzerland where heroin addicts are legally allowed to obtain heroin and shoot up. To them, the park is like a pub, the only legal heroin pub in the world! It is a way to get their fix openly and at the same time they socialise with other addicts whilst they are there! But they go back to the same park day in, day out. What would happen if they discovered that all of their friends were not going to the park that day, would they still go? Yes of course they would. Not to be sociable but to get the drug. These addicts never go to the park for the atmosphere, the weather, or the social life, they go for the drug. They feel better there than anywhere else, for everybody around them is doing the same thing. If there were only one pub where you could legally drink alcohol, you would go there. Not to be sociable, but simply to get your fix! I have been into a pub by myself on many occasions. I would get out my newspaper, have a drink, relax for a while and give myself a bit of peace and quiet. But I could have gone anywhere to do that, a library for example, it's a lot quieter there. I did not go to the library for one reason, they do not sell alcohol! Heroin addicts think that taking heroin is sociable. Crack heads think that taking crack is sociable. Alcohol addicts think that taking alcohol is sociable, as long as they are taking it at the same time, of course. I used to have such double standards when I was taking alcohol, as all drinkers do. I would say that alcohol is pleasurable and sociable, but if someone were taking the drug at a different time to me, I would immediately judge them. Don't all drinkers do that? Don't all drug addicts do that?

I needed to judge, it was a way to show myself and the world that I wasn't like them. I needed to prove that that I didn't need to drink in the morning, that I did not need to drink that much at that time. In truth, it was simply a way of saying *"Look everyone, this person is out of control with their alcohol intake, I am in control."* By pointing out what I believed to be **their** weakness, I was in fact trying to justify my own. It's the same with people who procrastinate all the time, their life becomes a mess, but if they see that *you* have put off one little thing, they will immediately pounce to condemn you for procrastination! You and I know that if somebody is drunk and you are sober, you hate it. You don't think that they are being sociable, confident, courageous, jolly people. You think the opposite of what the addict thinks. You think that they are being very un-sociable, annoying and stupid, and usually can't wait to get rid of them. If someone drinks eight pints in the pub at night, they are usually considered to be just a social drinker. If a businessperson downs half a bottle of scotch every night, he is considered to be an *alcoholic*. If somebody downs half a bottle of wine with lunch, nobody says a word, but if someone is on a bench drinking from a can of beer, they have a problem. All alcohol addicts judge other alcohol addicts. WHY? To make themselves feel better of course. All alcohol addicts are permanently condemning one another. I used to always say things like *"have you noticed how much so and so is drinking at the moment? She downed two bottles wine by herself last night, I think she might have a problem"* But on another occasion I would say *"Do you know what I am going to do tonight? I'm going to run a nice hot bath, crack open a good bottle of wine, and relax with a book"*. If I had said that I was going home to drink a bottle of wine by myself for the sake of it, that would have sounded as if I had a problem, but by making it sound good, (in other words *advertising* it in my mind and other people's), I could justify my intake of the drug. That is what all drug addicts do, they try and justify their own intake. Haven't you done this in the past? Haven't you judged people because they happen to be drinking at a different time to what you consider acceptable? Have you ever criticised someone else for apparently drinking too much? The alcohol addict's attitude is often "holier than thou" at times.

I was often guilty of doing this. The constant need to show that *I* did not have a problem. But of course I had a problem, all drinkers do, the alcohol is the problem! The biggest confusion for the poor drinker is that they really do not understand why they do drink although they know several reasons why they <u>shouldn't</u>. They fail to see the real reason for drinking. We are always justifying our intake and judging other people's intake. If we seem to be drinking less than others we feel in control, so we can state that we believe them to have a problem. This is odd when you think that many alcohol addicts brag about how they can "drink anyone under the table", yet the same people are permanently denying that they drink too much! How's that for a contradiction and hypocrisy!

I have said that I drank to be sociable, but what was sociable about drinking alcohol? Being sociable means interaction. How can you possibly interact with somebody who has lost all control of their senses? How can drinking alcohol increase your ability to socialise? It can't, it's yet another lie! The lie, or illusion, is created by the fact that you happen to be socialising whilst having a drink, consequently you believe that the drinking of alcohol is sociable. But, as I have explained it's the effect. Alcohol creates fear and insecurities, ones that were *never* there before we started to take the drug. The drinker feels awkward and slightly insecure without a drink at a social gathering. They have a drink and the insecure feeling goes away leaving them free to relax and socialise. The impression left is that alcohol took away certain insecure feelings. What the addict fails to see is that alcohol created them in the first place!

Not long after I'd stopped drinking I went to a place called Aberdovey, in Wales, for a water-skiing weekend with some friends. On the first night we all went to the pub, and I was asked what my "poison" was. I replied that I would like a pineapple juice and lemonade. The person who was buying the round responded by saying; *"No, come on, what are you having really?"* I thought that the last thing I wanted was to get into a discussion about not drinking, so I simply said that I was driving. This still wasn't good enough, as my friend stated that he was also driving, and that we could all leave our cars where they were and jump into the mini bus they had ordered to take us back to the hotel. I then explained that I wanted to start off with a 'soft' drink. Everybody then started to comment and ask what I intended to have after that. In the end I was forced to tell them that I didn't drink alcohol any more. I really don't know what reaction people get from their friends when they tell them that they are gay, but I can only imagine that it is a similar one to telling people that you have stopped drinking. I really had no idea how much interest and disbelief that this "admission" would cause, I felt as though I had just 'come out'.

The first question was inevitably *"Oh I didn't realise that you had a drink problem, are you an alcoholic?"* The question appears obvious, for we have been conditioned to believe that if you stop drinking for good it can only mean one thing, you have lost control and are an *alcoholic,* (or you have lost your mind!) This question is ridiculous when you analyse it, I don't drink any more, so how could I have a drink problem? The irony was that they were drinking alcohol *(taking the drug)* while asking me if *I* had a drink problem! You would think it odd if a heroin addict took heroin in front of you, offered you some and because you refused, commented that *"I didn't realise that* **YOU** *had a problem with heroin, are you a heroinolic?"* How pathetic would that be? Who would you think had the problem? Who would *anybody* think had the problem? You really don't need to be Sherlock Holmes to work it out do you?

My friends in Aberdovey reacted by saying things like *"Come on you boring bastard, what's the matter with you?"* *"You un-sociable git"* *"Let your hair down"* *"We are here to have fun"* and so it went on.

But at which point did I become boring? At which point did I become unsociable? At which point did I say that I wasn't going to have fun? Just before they asked me what I was having to drink, we were in the same place, talking, having a laugh and being **SOCIABLE**. So what had changed in the *second* that I said that I didn't drink alcohol any more? I was still the same person, I was happy, not being boring, and being sociable because I was out with people. The only thing that had changed was that the alcohol addicts could no longer just take their drug, without having to *think* about what they were doing. Hardly anybody who takes alcohol thinks about it, when they are in a room full of people taking the same drug at the same time. They are, after all, telling the same lies and believing them. I realised something that night that I never really expected up until that point. When I used to smoke and saw people around me who had stopped, I would envy them immediately, because I wanted to be like them.I knew that all smokers would love to stop, given the choice and that all smokers envied non-smokers. But I never thought that the same would apply to alcohol. Even when I was drinking and saw people who had stopped, or were on the wagon for a while, I never used to envy them, in fact there was a part of my brainwashed mind that actually felt sorry for *them*. I was, after all, suffering the delusion that they were missing out. The real problem was **so were they!** That is why I didn't envy these people when I was drinking; they were MISERABLE and DEPRESSED because they couldn't drink. They were pining for a drink and feeling deprived. Why on earth would you envy people like that? There is nothing to envy about feeling miserable, uptight, and depressed. As this is the image we have of people who don't drink, no wonder we are scared about 'giving up'. Unlike smoking, where there are now literally millions of ex-smokers out there who don't miss them, with alcohol the people who stop drinking on the whole still feel as though they have made a sacrifice. They still feel miserable and deprived.

However, there I was, out in a pub of all places, being sociable, laughing, talking, interacting, dancing, having a good time, not moaning about not having a drink but actually feeling elated because I didn't *have* to drink any more. I never realised that this was a totally new image for most people. This was why the people I was with actually started to envy me. They started to realise for themselves that I was still being sociable and doing all those previously mentioned things, but at the same time, not drinking, and not being a bore!

When you are taking a drug of any kind and somebody else isn't, you start to question why you need to do it and they don't, especially when they are happy not taking it. These friends started by saying that I was unsociable, boring and had a drink problem but finished by questioning their own drinking!

I digress slightly, I will return to 'other drinkers' in a later chapter. The point that I am making is that there is no such thing as 'sociable drinking'. When alcohol takes effect, you cease to be sociable, instantly! Being sociable means to interact with others. If you are doing this and not consuming alcohol you are still being sociable. What you shove down your throat doesn't make you sociable, it's what you say and how you interact. The 'sociable' aspect of alcohol is just another lie. I used to think that the consumption of alcohol was sociable because I would personally feel miserable, deprived and slightly insecure at times without it, I also felt a lot better around people who were taking the drug too. It's not that you even enjoy drinking at social gatherings, it's just that if you are not able to drink at one, you feel miserable and deprived. So the **choice** is simple, either miserable and deprived without, or reasonably happy with. You end up thinking that you are happy and sociable because of the drink, but that is *never* the case. Alcohol simply cannot make you happy or increase your ability to be socially compatible with others, it is yet another fallacy! It does the opposite.

Children do not need alcohol to throw a party. They do not need alcohol to socialise. Neither did you *before* you started taking it. If alcohol did even half of what we believed it to do for us, then all of society's problems would be solved by the consumption of alcohol wouldn't it? Why don't we encourage everyone to drink alcohol all the time, then we can unite in a world of no stress. A world where everyone is calm and relaxed. A world where everyone is happy and merry. A world without inhibitions. A world of courage and confidence. A world where everybody interacts and where there are no barriers. Wake up to the truth......... alcohol does NONE of these things! They are illusions that have been perpetuated for years and we have ended up believing them, that's all.

The sad reality is that the world in which alcohol is taken by the majority of people would be a world of beatings, rapes, violence, arguments, obnoxious and over emotional behaviour. It would be a world of stress. A world where <u>true</u> courage and confidence had been lost in a bottle or two. A world of suicides, murders, and muggings. A world of family hardship and abject poverty. That is what the world would look like if the majority of people drank alcohol. How do I know? Because it does!

I mentioned in this chapter that there is always a price to pay for taking alcohol, whether it's physical, psychological, social, or emotional. But what about the financial cost of alcohol, have you ever really worked out how much money you will spend because you are hooked on alcohol? I know I never did, but it is worth looking at your anything but ....

15

Liquid Asset

This fact will blow your mind, I know it did mine! The average drinker will spend roughly **ONE HUNDRED THOUSAND POUNDS** on alcohol in their lifetime! Let me just repeat that as it is a bit of an eye opener, "the average drinker will spend £100,000 on alcohol in their lifetime" WOW! That is a lot of money. Sometimes in my private consultations drinkers will say to me that they are not worried about the money. But why aren't we worried about £100,000? Drug addicts of any kind constantly delude themselves. We even fool ourselves into thinking that we have saved money when we are buying alcohol at times. For example, when you buy duty free alcohol, you always think "what a result, I've *saved* £30". We are always talking about a saving and never an expense. How on earth have you *saved* money when you have just spent £30? It is still £30 *more* than a non-drinker spends. This is only an average figure, for some it will be a lot more. I used to get through sixteen pints of lager a day at one stage, I was actually spending more on alcohol per day than I was being paid to work at the time! I would always wake up broke on a Monday morning. I would then have to sub some of my wages to pay for the next fix of my drug. I never saw it this way at the time, I was just a young lad who liked a beer, what was wrong with that? My wages at the end of the week were always pretty thin, as I had already drunk most of them during the week. When the weekend arrived it was time to really let my hair down and have a drink.

The situation changed slightly when I obtained a more professional job. I had more responsibilities, so I had no choice but to try and control my intake. I was never in control, but *felt* as though I was. I wasn't spending more than my wages on alcohol any more, (this was a major achievement) I was now a **'normal'** drinker. I was spending as "little" as everybody else. I never realised just how much alcohol addicts have to pay in real terms to get their drug. There is the direct financial cost of course, (around £100,000 as already stated). But what about all the additional expenses that nobody ever thinks about, which come about as a direct result of feeling dependent on alcohol?

First of all there are the taxi fares. One of the biggest joys of being free is being able to drive my car whenever I choose, to go to and from anywhere without having to worry about how or when I will arrive home, not even on New Year's Eve! I used to pay good money every month for my car, yet during my recreational time I couldn't drive it, because I was hooked on alcohol. I think back now to all those cold nights standing outside pubs and clubs waiting for a cab in my drunken state. It would cost me a fortune to get home, and the crazy thing was that I was paying for a car stranded outside my house. The average alcohol addict will spend roughly **EIGHTEEN THOUSAND POUNDS** on taxis in their lifetime as a direct result of alcohol.

Before you get in the taxi, you may have the additional expense of buying food, well stuff that they will tell you is food; as we all know, alcohol came first....kebabs second! The only reason that I would search out a curry house or kebab house, with a restaurant at the back, was simply to obtain more alcohol after hours. But again the 'food' is an additional expense. Next you have the expense of losing money in your drunken state, possibly down the back of the seat of the taxi, etc. You wake up in the morning with blood trying to pump through your dehydrated brain and your head is pounding away, so that you have to buy some more drugs to counter the effect of the drug alcohol (again this is more expense!). In addition, there is the cost of the flowers and cards to apologise for behaving like a complete idiot at certain times. Then you have the major expense of losing time at work. There are now 8 – 14 million working days lost in the U.K. each year, as a direct result of alcohol. For some, there is the cost of repair bills to their house where they have punched holes through doors, or smashed things in the house. For some, it's the cost of losing their licence, or the fines for being drunk and disorderly. For others, it's the huge financial cost of losing their jobs due to alcohol. The reality is that the financial cost when you see it in plain black and white is quite phenomenal. I really never thought about the money, alcohol was of course my *liquid asset*, (worth every penny, I thought). However, it was never an asset, far from it, in fact. I was paying good money to be mentally and physically abused by a product that in real terms did absolutely NOTHING for me! It was all just a clever confidence trick, perpetuating the biggest myth since it was claimed that the world was flat! Just because millions of people are paying through the nose for something they believe to be genuinely beneficial, doesn't mean that it gives them those benefits. Ninety nine percent of the population once believed that the world was flat; were they wrong to believe this? Were they lying to other people by telling them that the world was flat? The answer is no, the world does *appear* to be flat. Even when you are flying around the world, your perception is still that you are flying in a straight line, isn't it? (unless you are concord that is) I have never been into space to check for myself that the earth is round, but we now know for certain that it is. But doesn't this go completely against our own perception? In order to see the truth we have to move beyond how something *appears*. For years nearly everybody thought that it was flat, except one or two people. Mr Columbus said that he was going to sail *around* the world. Everybody thought he was insane. How can you possibly sail around something that is flat? Could he not see for himself the line in the distance that showed the edge of the earth? Everybody else could easily see it, why couldn't he?

People like Columbus and Gallileo moved beyond the accepted way of thinking and opened their minds. As a result they got to explore, and literally expand their horizons. They viewed things from a different perspective. By opening their minds and changing their perceptions they could see, as we all can now, that although the world may *appear* flat, it is really round. The flat world was just an illusion!

This book is all about changing your perception so that you can see the truth – alcohol does absolutely NOTHING for you at all. It only *appears* to give courage, happiness, confidence, relaxation and relief of stress. But it's all an illusion. Those who open their minds and see it clearly can really explore who they are and expand their horizons. Columbus experienced a life that many were too fearful to pursue. The only thing stopping those people was their *false* perception.

Even our government tells us that alcohol is good for us. Why do they keep perpetuating this blatant lie? Maybe it is because they are one of the biggest drug dealers in this country, if not the biggest! They are always talking about waging war on the drug pushers, yet they not only allow alcohol to be advertised, but they make a £10 BILLION profit every year from a drug which is known to kill FORTY THOUSAND people each year in the U.K. alone. I recently watched a documentary which stated that half a million pounds is spent on alcohol on a Saturday night in Newcastle alone! Some people will go without food to buy alcohol depending on how deep in the "quicksand" they are.

As mentioned, there are some people who are so brainwashed that they will spend hundreds or sometimes thousands of pounds for a bottle of wine, PLONKERS! (Pun intended) I used to pay a lot of money for a bottle of champagne; was the sparkling wine worth all that extra money simply because it was called "champagne?" No of course it wasn't, I was simply being a *plonker* myself for spending so much money on nothing more than sparkling wine.

I sometimes used to justify how much money I spent on drinking because I believed the biggest lie of all about alcohol …

14

A Little Of What You Fancy Does You Good?

This is without any doubt the biggest lie about alcohol. It is good for you!

Who tells us that alcohol is good for us? 'Experts' who are *alcohol addicts* themselves? But what does your body tell you? Wild animals have a very clever device to detect the difference between food and poison – their senses. We *also* have these incredibly clever devices. We do not need somebody with "qualifications" to tell us what is poisonous, our senses will do that for us. It has only recently been recognised that smoking is known to be incredibly harmful to the human body. But a few years back the 'experts' were telling us that smoking was good for us! It was usually the 'experts' who were smokers themselves. Perhaps they were attempting to justify their own intake of the drug. When somebody who has never smoked a cigarette lights up they cough, splutter, and are sometimes physically sick. What other health warning do you need? It is exactly the same with alcohol. When you had your first alcoholic drink how did your mind and body react? It made you feel physically and mentally sick. That is because it is a **POISON.** Alcohol is a poison that destroys the entire central nervous system and *INCREASES* blood pressure. It destroys brain cells, did you know that? Maybe you did know, but have forgotten! When you drink alcohol regularly you literally pound the brain. It is rather like going into a boxing ring every weekend and deliberately hitting yourself on the head over and over again. Is it good for you to destroy brain cells? Of course it isn't, the brain controls everything in your body, it tells your body how to work. If the brain cannot tell the body how to work it will become *sick*, not healthy. A friend of mine, who is a nurse, informed me that she was once present at something called a "Commando operation." The operation was on a man who had a tumour on the side of his face. It had spread so much that they had to remove virtually the side of his face plus part of his head. This exposed his brain during the operation. The surgeon said that the man was obviously a heavy drinker. My friend asked how he knew. He asked her to look at the size of the brain, it was a lot smaller than it was meant to be. This, he informed her, was a direct result of the patient's drinking.

ALCOHOL SHRINKS THE BRAIN!

The experts will tell us that alcohol is dangerous on the one hand, but that in small doses it can be good for people over the age of forty. How did they come up with this? We hear this kind of claptrap all the time and yet we never really question it. Why? Because it has been put across by the 'experts'. But does it make any sense at all? 'They' say that alcohol can *lower* blood pressure and that it can also *increase* blood pressure. It either does one or the other, how can it do both?

Alcohol kills 40,000 people a year in the U.K., what is healthy about that? They say that the health gains are for people over forty who may be protected against heart disease. Yet 90% of people over the age of forty drink alcohol, and heart disease is *still* the number one killer in the U.K. If alcohol helped fight against heart disease, as is the claim, then we should be the healthiest nation in the world and our incidences of heart disease would be almost obsolete! Kevin Lloyd, who played 'Tosh' in the television series 'The Bill', died of heart *failure*, along with hundreds of thousands of people throughout the world, because **of** the alcohol they consumed. It is not good for you, to say that it is is a blatant lie. You don't need to take my word for it either, just make up your own mind. Alcohol has been medically proven to:

Depress your entire central nervous system.

Undermine your courage, confidence, and your self-respect.

Destroy your brain cells.

Break down the immune system making you *less* resistant to all kinds of diseases. Interfere with the body's ability to absorb calcium resulting in bones that are weaker, softer, and more brittle.

Distort eyesight, making it difficult to adjust to different lights.

Diminish your ability to distinguish between sounds and perceive their direction.

Slur your speech.

Dull your sense of taste and smell.

Damage the lining of the throat.

Weaken the heart muscle and its ability to pump blood efficiently through the body. Inhibit the production of white and red blood bells.

Weaken muscles.

Destroy the stomach lining.

Irritate the lining of the intestines, which in turn causes ulcers, cancer, nausea, diarrhoea, vomiting, sweating, loss of appetite and loss of the ability to process nutrients and vitamins.

Overwork the liver, kidneys and pancreas.

Cause diabetes.

Cause obesity.

In short, how can anything, which is known to destroy every single organ in the human body, be called **GOOD** for you in any way shape or form? The crazy thing is that all this information is common knowledge to the 'experts' who are telling us that drinking is good for us! In fact alcohol is *just* as toxic to the human body as HEROIN! Let me repeat that as it is not a very well known fact:–

ALCOHOL IS JUST AS TOXIC AS HEROIN

Are they going to tell us that heroin is good for us? It is called in*toxic*ation for a reason.

They even talk about *sensible* drinking limits, SENSIBLE? How would you feel if they said that it wasn't sensible to get hooked and dependent on heroin, but in small amounts it is *sensible?* Would you believe 'them'? What really gets on my goat is that they even brainwash people into thinking that people who drink small quantities are healthier than non-drinkers. This is rubbish, a huge whopper of a lie, but it's been told for so long that even the medical profession thinks it's true. They argue that alcohol can help the blood not to clot, and yes alcohol does decrease production of blood clotting agents, but what they fail to tell us is THE BLOOD IS MEANT TO CLOT! Without the clotting uncontrolled bleeding can result in the liver and other areas. Do you think that someone who takes heroin in small amounts is healthier than a non-heroin addict? Do you think that the body is healthier with small amounts of poison going into it on a regular basis than a body that hasn't?

There is no such thing as *sensible* drinking, anyway. Have you ever seen anyone acting and talking sensibly when intoxicated? It's a contradiction in terms.

"But surely, if you drink for social reasons, then a little of what you fancy doesn't do you any harm, does it?" That is the same as saying "There is no harm in jumping into quicksand as long as you only go in up to your waist!" The nature of both is to drag you in one direction ... DOWN! The only difference between the two is that one is quick and obvious, the other is relatively slow, and to most, very subtle. There is no such thing as sensible DRUG taking, the only reason many doctors claim that alcohol is good for you and that the consumption of the drug is not an addiction, is largely because 'they' are hooked themselves. Virtually all doctors in the U.K. drink alcohol! I am not criticising them for this, they are in exactly the same trap that I found myself in, but because they cannot see for themselves that they are in a trap, they assume that there is no danger in taking alcohol in small doses. That is fine I guess because they may really have no idea that they are *not* in control, but to suggest that alcohol is actually good for you is nothing more than scandalous.

Alcohol, as I have already mentioned, is a DEPRESSANT. How can a depressant be good for you? This is one part of the brainwashing that I find most difficult to forgive. With all the other aspects of drinking 'they' could even be forgiven to a certain degree as they are hooked themselves and being deluded along with millions of others. But alcohol doesn't even have a warning on the label and is promoted by the health authorities as being GOOD for you. It is not seen as drug addiction. I was listening to an advert on the radio recently that warned about the dangers of the drug SPEED. It claimed that speed is psychologically addictive, and that the *user* would soon reach the stage where enjoyment would be increasingly difficult, if not impossible to achieve without it! But isn't that the same as alcohol?

Why aren't we warned about alcohol before we start taking it? Why aren't there adverts letting everybody know that alcohol is a highly addictive drug, with severe mental and physical side effects? Like everything else in this book, I want you make up your own mind, but remember that we were told that smoking was good for us years ago. Just because the human body is so ingenious that it builds up an immunity and tolerance to this poison, doesn't alter the fact that alcohol is a powerful poison and highly addictive drug which is not GOOD for you or anyone else for that matter! When you wake up after drinking alcohol do you feel good? When you see people vomiting in the street after they have taken alcohol do they look healthier than someone who doesn't drink? "Yes but surely a couple of glasses of red wine a day, for example, can be good for you?" NO IT CAN'T! The nature of any drug is to take more and more. Therefore when the medical profession make statements like "*a certain amount of units of alcohol a day are good for you but after you go past our guidelines it then becomes harmful*", they give the impression that people can control their intake. I have already said that this is a fallacy as the drug always controls its victim, whether the victim realises it or not. The drinker is having to exercise resolve on a regular basis not to increase. It only takes a very bad situation to occur in their lives and their resolve ends and they increase their intake. The more alcohol they take, the further down they go, the quicker they descend – the more they take! They end up in a loop. If you were to put small amounts of heroin into your body it wouldn't kill you either, but would it stop there? How many times have you only wanted to have a couple of drinks but ended up having more than you originally intended? All good intentions go out of the window when it comes to drug addiction, you want more and more, never less and less. Sensible heroin limits are 0 UNITS of heroin, sensible crack limits are 0 UNITS. These are the only sensible limits for any drug. The reason is that they are poisonous and addictive, which means you will quickly become psychologically dependent on them, and eventually reach the stage where you cannot cope without first having a fix of your drug. However, the sensible limits for alcohol vary throughout the world. Do people in the U.S. have different insides from us? Can the constitution of a Scandinavian cope better with more units of alcohol? That is what we are led to believe when we compare the recommended daily intake of units per day throughout the world. There is only one safe limit for any drug that will destroy you physically, mentally and emotionally and that limit is the same level recognised throughout the world for every other mind-altering drug- **'NO UNITS.'** *"It is healthy to put yourself in quicksand, just make sure you do not go in further than your waist!"* Now that would be a stupid statement for anybody to make, but can you imagine the medical profession saying it? *"It is OK to get HIV just make sure it doesn't develop into AIDS!"*

In 1985, £100M was spent treating alcohol-related diseases in the UK. That sounds healthy doesn't it?

I am not highlighting these health statistics to scare you into stopping, because that rarely, if ever, works. I remember when I was drinking heavily, my doctor told me that my liver would pack up by the time I was thirty, so the first thing I did was to have a drink to calm my nerves! Little did I know at the time that it was failing to calm me down at all. It was, in fact, doing the complete opposite. The reason for quoting these statistics is to stress the self delusion involved with drinking that has perpetuated for years and to help you see the product for what it actually is.

Everything I have just stated simply concerns the alcohol itself, not all the chemicals used to preserve it to make it appear drinkable! If you are a vegetarian, I bet you are not aware of the animal products in the wines and beers you are drinking. Even if you are *not* a vegetarian some of the things used to produce beers and wines will come as something of a surprise. Many wines are cleared using animal-derived ingredients. Clearing ingredients include isinglass, gelatine, egg albumen, modified casein (which is the high protein found in milk and used as one of the strongest wood glues known to mankind!), chitin (made from the shells of crabs and lobsters) or OX BLOOD! As for fortified wines, all ports except crusted port are treated using gelatine, and the colourant E120 (cochineal) also used in red wines and Campari. Cochineal is produced by extracting the red body material from insects – how lovely! Fish guts are also used in the processing of many wines. The chemicals used are too numerous to mention, but surely cannot be any good for us?

Another aspect of the brainwashing is that if you have already done the damage then it is too late. What is? Is it ever too late to stop putting a poison into your body? Is it ever too late to cure yourself of a disease? It is never too late to gain control of your life! The human body is without doubt a highly efficient survival machine, programmed to keep you alive. When you stop putting a poison like alcohol into your body, it literally breaths a sigh of relief. No matter how long you have been drinking, when you stop your body will start to repair immediately. The body can do one of two things when a poison enters the system, it can either store it, or get rid of it. It cannot store alcohol (if it did you would die), so it must get rid of it. The body wants to get rid of alcohol and will do so successfully as long as you don't put any back in. This brings me to another part of the alcohol brainwashing process. Your body is incapable of craving alcohol, no matter how long you've been drinking or what your intake is. Your mind and only your mind craves the benefits you believe alcohol gives you. A craving is nothing more than an internal representation of the way you perceive a product, perceive it as it really is and you do not have the craving.

I have mentioned that the physical and psychological slavery drug addiction are bad enough for the victims themselves, but there is one area that is rarely talked about or addressed, the people who suffer daily from the very harmful effects of...

17

Passive Drinking

 We hear all the time about the effects of passive smoking. We constantly hear about the crime which is caused by heroin, the houses being broken into so the addict can get hold of their next fix, the shootings which are 'drug related' etc. But what about the daily misery that many people suffer because of *passive drinking*?

Roy Castle highlighted the effects of passive smoking. He contracted lung cancer as a direct result of other people's smoke. I am here to highlight the effects of a new phenomenon, one which causes more harm than passive smoking ever has done or ever will do – *passive drinking*. The sad truth is that there is hardly a single person who hasn't suffered, or isn't suffering right now, from the very dangerous effects of *'Passive drinking'*.

Passive drinking is the harm caused to someone that is a direct result of other people's drinking.

We often judge the person who feels the need to drink from morning until night for the harm they inflict on their family and others around them. There are even support groups set up for the families who fall victim to passive drinking, the families who live with what society has labelled an *alcoholic*. However, what we often fail to realise, is the effect that *all* drinking has on other people:–

The beatings, the divorces, the violence, the neglect, the emotional hurt, the direct physical hurt, the sexual abuse, the suicides, the murders, the stabbings, the mood swings, the outbursts, the arguments, the unwanted pregnancies, the financial ruin, the pain, anguish and misery caused by the effects of *passive drinking* are second to none.

I recently treated a young man for alcohol addiction. He had also been sold the idea that he was an alcoholic and was very desperate to stop. One of the reasons for wanting to quit was that he had beaten up his own father only a few weeks before, whilst under the influence. He could hardly recall the incident and clearly would NEVER have done it if he hadn't been drinking. The reason for this was that it wasn't <u>him</u>. He was 'under the influence' of something that was controlling what he did and what he said. He was due to appear in court three days before Christmas. His father was not drinking, but had suffered at the hands of somebody who had been – his own son. He not only suffered the physical harm, but also the emotional hurt caused by his son. In other words he suffered physically and mentally as a direct result of *passive drinking!*

A teenage boy woke up to find his best friend lying next to him in a pool of blood. He had stabbed him the night before, but could not recall a thing. The boy was just eighteen years old at the time and had only been on a 'lads" night out. He blacked out because of the alcohol and is now serving a life sentence for murder. Was the murder 'drug related'? Was it even murder? Did he know what he was doing? He was not in control of mind or body, he was under the influence. Is this a made up story? NO! Is this a one off accident? NO! Incidences like this are happening EVERYDAY throughout the world. How many more people are now suffering the effects of *passive drinking* because of this one incident, caused directly by alcohol?

Firstly there are the two families of both victims. Both the dead teenage boy and the boy who committed the crime are victims. Their families' grief, sorrow and anger will be there every day until the day they die. The friends who have lost their companions and the people who lost their staff or colleagues also suffered. The paramedic who found the teenager's dead body would have to live with that image for the rest of his life and the boy who committed the "*murder*" will now be suffering every day for the rest of his life. He will wake up each morning, having lost his best friend, knowing that he killed him. Then there is the cost to the state of keeping him in an over crowded prison system for a crime he can't remember committing. All this pain and suffering as a result of two boys wanting a fun night out: what possible harm could that do?

You may think that this is a very dramatic incident and argue that in such situations there are many other factors, like the boy's personality, for example. Some people believe that you have to be 'that way inclined' in the first place, you cannot simply blame such behaviour on alcohol. YES YOU CAN! If somebody commits a crime whilst they are on crack cocaine or heroin, people immediately say it's because of the drug. They immediately say that the crime is *drug related* and the perpetrators are offered help. However, if it's alcohol they get a prison sentence!

When somebody on L.S.D. jumps from a roof believing that they can fly, do we assume that it is in their nature to jump from roofs, or is it more likely to result from having taken the drug? I have said and done things that I would NEVER normally do when I was 'under the influence' and so has every single person who has ever drunk alcohol. That is the nature of the beast.

When you say things you would never normally say, or do things that you would never normally do as a result of alcohol, then inevitably somebody close by will suffer from the effects of passive drinking. It would be difficult to know just how many people are affected by this phenomenon.

Sarah Collins suffered so much from passive drinking that she took her own life because of it. Sarah is the unfortunate mother who committed suicide three years after a wine drinking session ended with the death of her daughter.

Sarah Collins never recovered from the guilt of giving her **six year old** daughter wine which killed her. Stacey (her daughter) had so much alcohol in her body that her blood alcohol level was more than twice the drink-drive limit. This may sound shocking, you may even find yourself judging Sarah for what she did. But I was given wine with a meal as a child. In France it's seen as abnormal *not* to give children a little taste of wine with dinner. Sarah's predicament was as a result of her being under the influence at the time, she simply was not aware that Stacey was going into the kitchen every five minutes to have some more wine.

The sad reality is that Stacey would have suffered from the effects of alcohol long before she took that first fatal drink. People are fooled into thinking that it's only *alcoholics* who neglect their families and cause heartache to the people they come into contact with. However, the truth is that everybody who has ever drunk alcohol has caused other people either physical or emotional harm as a direct result of their drinking. Most of the time they will not be aware of the distress they have caused as they are under the influence at these times. But in each case the third party has fallen victim to *passive drinking*.

Children suffer all the time from the effects of passive drinking. They are frequently left to wait in the car with a coke and straw while the 'adults' go into the big building for grown ups only. They suffer the embarrassment of seeing their parents get over emotional, falling over, or being sick. They see them getting loud, argumentative, aggressive, or abusive to each other or directly to them. They feel upset as they lie in bed at night, listening to alcohol fuelled arguments or hearing the sound of physical abuse. These are feelings of neglect and hurt when they cannot communicate properly with their parents who are in a drunken state. They may desperately wish that their parents would return to normal so that they can talk to THEM and not to these 'other people' who they wish would go away. Children frequently suffer verbal abuse during a parent's hangover and wonder what they have done to cause it. They miss days out because their parents were suffering from a hangover, or didn't have the money because of the cost of taking their drug on a regular basis.

All children hate to see their parents drinking, I know I did. There is nothing more embarrassing and hurtful to a child than seeing your mother or father in a drunken state. If you did manage to talk to your parents in their drug induced state, then you would either have them telling you they love you every two seconds, or hear shouting and abuse about how everything that has ever happened is your fault! What's wrong with the first scenario? What is wrong with somebody letting you know how much they love you? If you have been there you will know exactly what is wrong with it; *they* are not telling you they love you, because it's not really them. They are 'under the influence' of a drug. This is not true affection, it's hurtful and embarrassing. The **majority** of child abuse cases are directly related to alcohol (and that is just what is reported). If a child has a parent on whom they depend and that parent is dependent on alcohol, then who can that child depend on? Obviously it's not just the children who suffer from passive drinking; the whole family feels the physical, mental, and financial burden of having an addict in the family. These are just examples of people who suffer inside the home, there are many other people who are affected by passive drinking. 50% of all adult pedestrians killed in road accidents are twice over the drink drive limit! Not the driver, the pedestrian! The driver who knocked them down has to suffer for the rest of his or her life, blaming himself or herself and desperately wondering what could have been done to avoid the pedestrian. A life time is spent suffering terrible guilt and regret. The accident and emergency services suffer the passive drinking effects all the time, not only through treating the patients who have been injured as a direct result of alcohol, but also from physical and mental abuse from patients who are on alcohol...the very people they are trying to help! Many hospitals now find it necessary to recruit extra security on Friday and Saturday nights. 98% of physical abuse towards doctors and nurses is alcohol related, that's NINETY EIGHT PERCENT! The police also have to cope with an extra workload at weekends, resulting from alcohol related incidents. Then there are the victims of drunk driving who suffer daily because of the effects of passive drinking. As well as the person injured or killed outright, families, friends, and colleagues will be affected for the rest of their lives because of the tragedy. Then of course there are the other victims, the drivers themselves. The driver may wake up night after night in a cold sweat, reliving the moment over and over again in their minds and praying everyday that they could just turn back the clock.

Whole nations have suffered from passive drinking, including our own. England taught the world how to play football but were then banned from Europe for years because of the alcohol induced behaviour of "supporters". The 1998 World Cup in France once again resulted in violence from many different nations, but mainly England and Germany. Every single person arrested had been drinking alcohol, could this have been coincidence? Of course not, it's an evil drug that removes people's fear and causes death and destruction. England stood a good chance of hosting the World Cup in the year 2006, but the chances are now very slim...why? Because of alcohol induced thuggery. A whole nation is suffering the effects of passive drinking. It cost Paul Gascoigne (English Footballer) his life's dream, a chance to play in the final of a World Cup. He didn't get to play in <u>any</u> of the games because of his drinking!

The rest of the team were also the victims, they were being deprived of one of the greatest footballing talents of all time.

If you are a non-smoker, you no longer have to suffer the effects of passive smoking at 30,000 feet, smoking is now banned on nearly every major airline. However, even at 30,000 feet you can still be affected by *passive drinking*. It is now widely referred to as *air rage*. British airways have even had to incorporate a 'yellow card' policy for drunk and disruptive passengers after an air rage incident in 1998. Many passengers were in fear as John Henson went into a drunken rage. During one hour of mid-air mayhem he threatened to kill the pilot and head butt a passenger, then smashed a seat and indecently assaulted a stewardess. Staff and passengers had to wrestle him to a seat where he was handcuffed and strapped in by his ankles. Maybe they should have given him a drink to calm him down!

There are so many people who have literally been disfigured for life due to passive drinking. I was standing in a pub once when one man accidentally stepped onto the foot of another. (This is easy to do when you have had a drink!) Next time I saw the man who accidentally stumbled, he was lying outside the pub with his right eye resting on the pavement next to him. The other man had shoved a glass into his face for treading on his toe. The effects of passive smoking can take years to materialise – the effects of passive drinking are often instant!

I have realised whilst writing this chapter that I could write another book on the effects of passive drinking alone. The whole point of this chapter is for you to open your mind and start to wake up to the truth about this drug. You must realise that the beatings, divorces, the violence, the neglect, the emotional hurt, and direct physical hurt, the sexual abuse, the suicides, the murders, the stabbings, the mood swings, the outbursts, the financial ruin, the accidents, the drownings, the pain, the anguish and sheer misery caused by the effects of *passive drinking* are second to none.

But, after all, what does that matter, every good night out on alcohol always has a happy ending doesn't it? When you think about it you can usually look back at most events where alcohol is concerned and laugh about them can't you? After all everybody knows that most nights on alcohol are just a ......

18

Barrel Of Laughs

 You know, I always thought that alcohol was a bit of a laugh. You can always look back and laugh at some of the ridiculous situations that have occurred due to alcohol, and to be fair, some appear quite funny. But are they? Is this yet another way of covering up our stupid and destructive behaviour, when on alcohol. Well, as I have said throughout the book, make up your own mind.

Alcohol stories tend to involve people making complete fools of themselves, which turn into funny stories to be related over and over and over again. Throughout the years that people drink, they may only have about half a dozen 'alcohol stories' anyway. The problem is that you hear them repeated again and again. Nearly all drinkers have at least one alcohol story up their sleeves, very rarely do they have more than half a dozen. It doesn't really occur to drinkers that they have told the same stories for years, that they have drunk alcohol for years and can still only think of a few alcohol related 'funny' stories. I know that I used to do this, but then alcohol does destroy brain cells, so maybe I just forgot that I had told the same stories a thousand times over to the same people! But were they ever funny in the first place?

I woke up one morning when I was just seventeen years old to discover that the night before I had run stark naked through my mother's house where all of my friends were, then went out into the middle of the road and tried to spin on my head! (This was when break-dancing was all the rage) It was midnight and I was totally naked! Funny? Well no, not really. I could have easily broken my neck that night and been confined to a wheelchair for the rest of my life, now that really would have made a funny story wouldn't it? I have told that story for years with the usual "Oh yeah, but guess what happened to me?" beginning. The truth is that I didn't remember a thing, I had a 'black out'. I have never forgotten the story simply because of the embarrassment that it caused me for years. Nearly, perhaps, as much embarrassment as the poor young man who woke up in the middle of the night to find himself half way through urinating over his parents feet as they slept in their bed one evening. He was awoken by his mother's screams and then saw the look of sheer horror from his Dad. He was just sixteen at the time and ran away from home, FUNNY though isn't it?

For years I have told a 'funny' story about when I stole (borrowed for a little while) my uncle's van one night and was too drunk to remember that I hadn't learnt how to drive yet! I was in first gear all the way home. When I woke up, I remembered what had happened, but couldn't get the van back as I realised that I couldn't actually drive! When I looked at the van I could see that front was smashed up and as soon as I saw this I began to experience flashbacks from the drive home. I was driving down a hill and a policeman had tried to stop me, by standing in the middle of the road. I swerved to avoid him and hit a bollard in the middle of the road. How I actually managed to get back home is still a mystery.

FUNNY?

"Do you remember when I was so drunk that I fell asleep on the train and ended up in the middle of nowhere at seven o'clock in the morning, no money, cold, hungover and it took me all day to get home?"

FUNNY?

"Do you remember when Peter drove the wrong way down a one way street and was too drunk to realise?" FUNNY? *"Yeah but what about when Jill vomited in Nick's lap at that dinner party?"* Hysterical? *"Yeah, but what about when Tom was handcuffed to a lamppost stark naked and left out in the freezing cold for hours?"*

FUNNY?

There seems to be a real competition amongst drinkers as to who has the funniest alcohol story. I mean, you really are just not a drinker until you have at least once...forgotten where the toilet was and urinated in some outrageous place, or vomited over your spouse's parents. Fallen off a balcony and cracked a rib. Fallen asleep on a bus, train, or whichever mode of transport that was meant to take you home but instead ended up in a field lying face down in a cow pat. Slept with somebody who resembled the picture of beauty itself the previous night, only to realise the next morning that you have in fact just slept with the creature from the hounds of the Baskervilles! Got the boot from work at least once because you were too hung over to go in, or because too many at lunch meant fluffing your work or being rude to a colleague or client! Phoned everybody in your phone book at 3am, in your drunken and lonely state or fallen asleep at least once in the middle of having sex! Unless you have done at least one or maybe all of these you are just not a drinker! You see, alcohol addicts try to justify their behaviour by turning it into a laugh whenever possible.

It's funny how alcohol addicts don't sit around laughing about the arguments, the beatings, the violence, the abuse, etc...and all too often even the stories that were made into jokes were never funny in the first place. The person who slept with the creature from the "Hounds of the Baskervilles", suddenly gets a phone call to say that they are pregnant! The person who lost their way and ended up in a cow pat, suddenly realises that they have missed work again and have now lost their job!

Am I implying that I don't find some of these alcohol stories funny, have I lost my sense of humour? NO NO NO, of course some of are funny, but seeing somebody trip over is amusing too. I once watched a friend of mine go to look out of a window, but because it was so clean, he put his head straight through the pane of glass! This isn't really funny, but I can't tell the story with a straight face! (he wasn't hurt, in case you were wondering).

The point is that alcohol addiction is anything but a 'barrel of laughs'. We laugh at some things that occur as a result of alcohol simply because they show somebody who is out of control. The stories are simply part of the facade of justifying drug taking. No doubt heroin addicts joke about how they once missed a vein and hit an artery – Funny?

Or how they were so 'out of it' they nearly choked on their own vomit! FUNNY?

The thing about alcohol stories is that they are told by people who can rarely recall the event themselves and are simply telling you what happened afterwards, or what other people have told them that they did. A friend of mine left a party ten minutes before I was going to give him a lift home recently. We were staying at his place and I had a key to get in. When I arrived there was no sign of him. When I woke in the morning, there was still no sign, but later that afternoon a movement came from his room. He came out with dried blood down the back of his head. I asked him what had happened. He said that he had caught a bus home, but that the next thing he remembered was waking up miles from home with blood pouring from his head. No doubt that will turn into a funny story in no time at all.

This is without doubt one of the biggest gains of being FREE, to be able to remember everything, every part, every second of this very precious life, and to always be in full control, with the knowledge that you are seeing everything through a …

19

Clear Head!

 Of all the joys of being truly free, one of the greatest is having a clear head at all times. When I have good time, I know that it is *genuine*. I am able to remember the nights out – *all* of them. I can remember every conversation, every event, every minute of everyday. I wake up and feel AWAKE! What a concept! I have *true* confidence back and *true* courage. I no longer wake up wondering what I've done the night before. I never ever have a hangover. Let me emphasise that;

I NEVER EVER HAVE A HANGOVER!

I am always refreshed, alert and alive. I have the genuine choice to utilise every single one of these precious days that we have whilst we are here. I am able to drive my car whenever I choose to! I now have the freedom to go out every night if I choose to, without the worry of having to exercise control over my drug intake! I am able to go dancing until the early hours and still feel good the next day. I no longer *have* to spend my hard-earned money pouring poison down my own throat, a poison that controlled so many aspects of my life. I never *have* to take alcohol in order to enjoy or cope with my life. I no longer have to say sorry to people for my outrageous behaviour at times when I was 'out of it' (most of which I could never remember doing anyway) I suddenly have tremendous amounts of the most precious commodity – time. I never lose time because of the effects of either being on the drug or the mental and physical effects of trying to eliminate the drug. To me, everyday is now as precious as the next. I now have more money, much, much, much better health, more peace of mind, more self respect, more courage, more confidence and tons more FREEDOM. All of these are the benefits of a life free from alcohol addiction.

The biggest gain of all, is to be mentally and physically FREE forever.

I once had a person in one of my sessions who asked me *"If alcohol was free of charge and didn't do any harm to you or others, would you drink again?"* The answer was without hesitation, "NO WAY, NEVER, NOT IN A MILLION YEARS". They had to ask again, they said *"did you mishear, I said if alcohol was free of charge and there were no health risks involved, would you drink again?"* Again I said "NO WAY, NEVER, NOT IN A MILLION YEARS". The reason is because the difference is like night and day. As you are already aware, and all drinkers know, alcohol costs a fortune and causes you and others around you harm. However, it's the daily mental and physical slavery that never really occurs to drinkers. It's the *having* to have a drink in order to enjoy or cope with your life. It's the *having* to work your life around when can you have the next fix. It's the very lack of genuine freedom and genuine choice that never really dawns on drinkers. I always said that I chose to drink and I believed that to be true. But what genuine choice is there when you have to do something in order to cope or enjoy your life. It is freedom from this dependency that is the greatest gain. Most alcohol addicts delude themselves that only what society labels *alcoholics* have a dependency on alcohol and have lost control.

My point is that if you have to exercise control, then you *are* dependent and are never really in control anyway. Why would you want to have this constant battle to exercise control over something that does absolutely nothing for you at all?

That is why I will never drink again. I am now in true control once more. I no longer have this battle to exercise control on a weekly, if not daily basis. I was always on to a loser like every drinker, as the drug was always controlling me. The fact that I didn't realise this, most of the time, never changed the reality. TO BE BACK! That's what it feels like, to be back in full control over every area of my life. You really have no idea just how much alcohol is ruling, and controlling many aspects of your daily life (even when you are in-between fixes) until you stop. As I said it is like night and day.

Every time I went to a party after a few in the pub, my first thought was not who would be there, but to wonder whether there would be any drink left. If there wasn't, I would not enjoy myself – I couldn't, not without my drug. Before I spoke to anyone at a social gathering, I would have a drink first. I would, on many occasions, NOT go and have a laugh because I knew that I would drink, so I stayed in because I didn't want to. But if I didn't want to drink, why couldn't I just go out and not have a drink? It was because I was not in control, the drug dictated where I went or whether I enjoyed myself. That is dependency!

To no longer be dependent is one of the best feelings in the world. I was dependent on a substance that in real terms did absolutely nothing for me at all. I just couldn't see it myself as I was locked in a world that appeared real. If you see things from an outside point of view, it becomes incredibly easy to see. But if you are locked in a world that you are convinced is real, how will you ever know? The Hollywood actor Jim Carrey starred in a film that fooled his perception too. Let me explain a bit about the anything but ....

20

Trueman Show

If you haven't seen this film I will explain. I'm no Barry Norman, but please bear with me. Hollywood has created the ultimate soap opera. The difference is that one of the characters in the film, "Truman" played by Jim Carrey, has no idea that his whole life is being watched by the rest of the world, twenty four hours a day. They call it *"The Truman Show"*. There are cameras in his house, in his car, in fact everywhere he goes. Nothing is real in this world, not even the sea or the sky. His whole family are actors, including his wife. His work place and home are just part of the biggest film set ever created. It is the ultimate voyeur's dream, a 24 hour live "fly on the wall" insight into someone's life. It is the most watched television programme of all time and the makers are keen to keep it going for as long as possible. They are making millions out of controlling his existence and if they manage to keep the illusion going until he dies he will be none the wiser. Just like a real soap opera there are script writers planning what should happen next. Truman himself believes that the world he is in is real and every decision he makes is of his own choice and doing. And why shouldn't he? He has no idea that his life is being controlled and his very destiny is in the hands of a script writer.

However, the makers of *The Truman Show* didn't take into account one eventuality, he wants to explore the world. The show is thirty years old and so is Truman himself. There is a part of him that knows that there is more to life than where he is and he wants to expand his horizons. This is a major problem as there is nowhere to travel to. He lives in a world within a world, but has no idea. The sea only goes so far and eventually hits the edge of the film set. But how is Truman to know? The makers of the TV show do everything in their power to stop him. Truman's father was killed in a fishing accident when he was just a boy. Truman has always blamed himself for the death and has not been able to go over water since. His father was, like everybody else, just an actor who is really alive and well. The creator of *The Truman Show* had to think of something to stop him travelling. Killing his father and making him scared of water seemed like a good plot for the live soap. The next option for Truman was plane travel. However, when he went to the travel agents there were pictures of planes crashing and he was told that it is the most dangerous way to travel. His actress wife is constantly telling him not to go and travel but to start a family. To cut a long story short, several events occur that lead him to sense that something is not quite all it seems in this world. He finally made a decision to cross the sea by boat, there was just no other alternative. The director panics and creates a storm (literally) where Truman nearly dies. They cannot let him leave or let him die live on television. In the end, through storms and much more his boat ends up hitting the sky, which after all was just a large piece of heavy canvas. It was at this moment his perception began to change. He climbed out of the boat and put his hand on the sky! He then found some stairs leading to a door in the middle of the sky. He opened the door and knew at this point that he had discovered a whole new world he never knew existed. However, there was still fear. Truman had only known that world and did not know what was out there. The illusions had been removed, but there was a voice telling him that there is nothing out there that is not already here. The voice was that of the creator of the programme, trying one last attempt to save his precious programme. Although Truman felt a little fearful, what was his alternative? Stay in a world where everything is false for the rest of his life! What kind of life is that? There really was no decision to make, he thought for a second and then in a truly confident manner he voiced his catch phrase "Farewell. And if I don't see ya again, good afternoon, good evening and GOOODNIGHT!"

His life and destiny changed at that point and he became his own script writer. For thirty long years everything that he believed was false. But just because he strongly believed it was real, did not make it so. Everybody on the outside knew it was all false, but to one person in the world it *appeared* very real. When the creator of the show was asked afterwards in an interview why did he think that it took Truman so long to realise what was really happening, he replied –

"We accept the world with which we are presented"

And how true is that?

For many years I strongly believed that everything that alcohol *appeared* to do was real. I thought that it was all True! However, I was simply being deceived, but I was not the only one. I was *accepting a world with which I was presented*. In the film, Truman was the only person who was being deceived and controlled. He was just one person who was suffering from delusion. When it comes to alcohol there are millions throughout the world who are being deluded. I realised when I escaped that there is a whole new world out there. If you were Truman, and let's say that you were not the only one being fooled but your whole family were being deluded, would you just watch like everybody else from the outside once you found this whole new world, or would you do everything in your power to make them see so they could also be set free? You want to do everything in your power to help them see that they were being deluded and that they were trapped.

That is exactly how I feel. I can see it so clearly now and this book is about helping you to see something that is so obvious when you look beyond the accepted perception.

The good news is that when you stop drinking you begin to write your own script and control who *you* are and you do not have to go through a storm of any kind, contrary to the brainwashing. There is a door in the sky that literally releases you to a whole new world and the key is in your own head, you are your own jailer. The only thing that is stopping you is fear. I could have escaped years before I did, but fear stopped me. The false perception created by the alcohol itself and the brainwashing since birth.

Another way to see beyond the false perception is to really mentally step outside the cage for a minute and ask the question .....

21

Am I A Man Or A Mouse?

A mouse is put in a cage and given food, water and a liquid drug. There is a button to the side of a metal funnel where the liquid drug would be dispensed. In order for the mouse to get the drug it must hit a button with its nose first. There is food and water, but out of *curiosity* the mouse hits the button. The mouse has its first dose of the drug. It squeals loudly and its body reacts horribly to the poison. (Similar to when a human has its first dose of a liquid drug). The scientist then removes the food and water and the mouse is left only with the drug. Having no choice the mouse then hits the button and drinks the liquid drug. After a while the mouse goes back and hits the button again during the withdrawal period. In other words, as the drug is leaving the mouse's body. The mouse does not have the same reaction to the drug. This time it does not squeal and appears to have no adverse physical reaction to the drug. In truth, the mouse now feels slightly better than a moment before as the drug has now momentarily suppressed a feeling that it caused. The mouse has no idea, but the liquid drug is designed to destroy its central nervous system. The mouse hits the button again during the withdrawal period and feels better than a moment before. The scientist then puts the food and water back into the cage. The mouse takes some, but then goes straight for the button. After a while the mouse ignores the food and water altogether and just continues to hit the button. In no time at all you start to see the mouse's body shaking. When it hits the button, it stops shaking and very quickly its nervous system begins to be affected again. The shakes start again and what does the mouse do? Hit the button! Does the mouse feel better? Yes! But only better than it did a moment before and nowhere near as good as it felt before it started to push the button in the first place. The poor mouse has no idea, its central nervous system is slowly being destroyed by the drug, but it is tricking the mouse into thinking that it's helping. The more it shakes the more it hits the button, the more it hits the button the more it shakes. The mouse builds up such an immunity and tolerance to the drug that even whilst it hits the button it still shakes, just slightly less than a moment before. After a while the mouse just continues to hit the button, hit the button, hit the button, until it dies.

This is an actual experiment that is routinely carried out in drug tests. I do not condone this type of practice in any way shape or form, but when I saw this experiment it dawned on me that this was exactly what I was doing when hooked on alcohol. Once you hit the button a couple of times you really do become the mouse. But just like the mouse you cannot see it whilst you are pushing the button. The drug appears to have the opposite effect to what it is really doing. The drug was suppressing my nervous system so much that I believed in the end I could not enjoy myself or be as confident at a social gathering without a drink. The insecurities I had were *caused* by alcohol. It was the drug and only the drug that had done that to me. Now I am out of the cage it is easy to see. This book is about stepping outside yourself so that you can see what is really happening. If the mouse had that opportunity to see what it was actually doing, do you think that it would continue? The mouse doesn't have the rational sense to analyse its actions, human beings do!

So the question really is are you a Hu*Man* or a *Mouse*?

Well then, it's time to ...

22

Lose Your Bottle And Gain Your Courage!

 Just like the mouse and the scientist I now realise that I only had to look at other people when they were drunk to know that alcohol doesn't actually do anything. But I was a *mouse* and 'under the influence'. I believed in the alcohol world. A world within a world; a world that had created a set of false fears to con me into thinking that I couldn't escape; a world that deluded me into thinking I could not enjoy or cope with my life as much without it. I had the *bottle* but had lost my *true* confidence! When I finally lost my bottle (and can!) I gained it back.

One of the biggest joys of being totally free, is to actually be in a position where any moments of stress have now become exciting challenges once again. As you are now aware, alcohol *causes* stress; physical, mental, emotional and financial. Because I am now physically, mentally, emotionally and financially much better off than before, I can now easily deal with stress as it happens, instead of doing an impression of an ostrich every time a challenge comes along. And more importantly, I do not have as much stress to deal with anyway. Once you are free you gain true courage and have true confidence again, this means that you are a lot more capable of dealing with anything that comes along. Stress only becomes stress if you are not strong enough to handle it, and if you are slave to a drug like alcohol you will *always* be more mentally and physically depressed than you ever would be as a person that doesn't _need_ to drink.

It is so wonderful to be able to have genuine relaxation where my mind <u>and</u> body are totally calm and relaxed. This is instead of either feeling the effects of the drug itself, the stress of trying to get over the symptoms of the drug (withdrawal), the stress of feeling guilty because I needed the drug, or the stress of thinking about when I can next take the drug. Am I implying that you will never get stressed again after you stop drinking? NO, of course not, there are good and bad days whether you are a drinker or a person who doesn't drink. But physically and mentally you will be so much stronger that the highs will be much higher and the lows nowhere near as low as they used to be. If somebody smashes into my car I don't say _"that's OK I'm a non-drinker"_, I still get uptight. The difference is that I am much better equipped to deal with it and I do not feel the need to turn to a drug to solve that problem – I now turn to a mechanic!

It is so nice to be the scientist and not the mouse!

The truth is that when you put your mind outside the cage you soon start to see the obvious. The only reason why the mouse was hitting the button was to try to end a low. The only reason why people drink alcohol is also to try and end a low. Perhaps the _low_ is lack of self confidence, courage, or self respect. They may drink to help with inhibitions, shyness, insecurity, lack of concentration, stress, boredom, deprivation, or just plainly and simply to end the low of not being able to enjoy themselves without the drug. The problem is that alcohol _causes_ all of these lows. It never genuinely relieves them or solves them.

I used to believe that I loved drinking, I would walk in to a pub order a pint and think "lovely!" Why did I feel so much better just for holding it in my hand? I felt better and yet the alcohol hadn't had time to take effect! So why did I feel better? Because like any other drug addict, I was so psychologically hooked that I simply didn't have the courage to stand there without my drug, I would have felt very deprived and uptight if I couldn't do it. Most of the week I was _having_ to control my intake and on Saturday nights I didn't. So just having the drink without having to discipline myself made me feel happier and calmer. But I should have been happy anyway! Having to exercise control, having to use willpower and discipline over your alcohol intake is a LOW! Ending a low of any kind can *appear* pleasurable. But what was I enjoying? The drink had not taken any effect physically only mentally!

It is so clear when you look at it with an open mind. The relaxing drinks are the ones taken at relaxing times. The drinks that make you happy are taken at happy times. The drink *never* changes only the situations. It is always the situation that is special, never the drink.

It had destroyed my courage and confidence so subtly, every week for so many years that I wasn't aware of it, but all the time I thought it was doing the opposite. I had been conditioned from birth to believe that alcohol helps people to enjoy their lives; that it helps to give them courage, helps them to relax and gives confidence. But I can now see very clearly that they are not so much happy *with* alcohol, or more relaxed, or more confident *with* alcohol, but very miserable, unconfident, and unrelaxed *without* it! The alcohol itself simply creates all the illusions and, backed up by the massive brainwashing since birth, we believe the illusions to be true. It is such a clever confidence trick, but that is all it is, a trick, a CON!

If you feel miserable without alcohol and happier with it, you are going to conclude that you are happy because of the alcohol. But as I have repeated throughout this book, IT DOES THE COMPLETE OPPOSITE. In fact everything you thought and have been conditioned to believe that alcohol does for you, think of the complete opposite and you will find the truth. I can now see so clearly that EVERY TIME I drank alcohol, I was simply trying to get to a position where I was as confident, as happy, as relaxed, as secure and as normal as I was *before* I started taking the drug! I could easily get there again simply by fully understanding that there was nothing to give up and by *not* taking the drug ever again. In other words I was drinking to try and feel like a person who doesn't NEED to drink, already feels!

I was drinking to feel like a non-drinker! (normal person)

Look at people who have never drunk alcohol, (there aren't many of
them in this country. Some of the only examples are children! But
there are some adults who have never drunk alcohol) they go to
parties and enjoy themselves, they lie in a bath and relax, they have
confidence, they have courage. When you drink and are in exactly the
same social situation as they are, you are never happier than they are.
When you are relaxing with a drink you are *never* more relaxed than a
non-drinker in the same situation. You never have more courage or
confidence when drinking than a non-drinker in the same situation.
The sad reality is that you have a great deal less!

Alcohol suppresses your entire central nervous system, your
courage, confidence and self respect. So the person who doesn't
need to drink wins hands down every single time. When they are
happy, it's *true* happiness, when they are relaxed it's *true*
relaxation, when they are confident, it's *true* confidence. When you
drink it's all false! Why do you feel as though you *need* alcohol and
they don't? It's because of the drug itself and the brainwashing.
ALCOHOL CREATES FEAR AND INSECURITIES. These feelings
keep people hooked on something that they wish they didn't need.
It is fear that social gatherings cannot be enjoyed without alcohol,
fear that you cannot cope with many aspects of your life without
alcohol, fear that you cannot get fully relaxed without alcohol, fear
you will have inhibitions without it, fear that you will always be
miserable and feel deprived without alcohol, fear you will be lacking
in confidence without alcohol, fear that your character will change
without it, or the worse fear that we have been conditioned to
believe, the fear that you can NEVER get truly free from alcohol
addiction. But as I will repeat once more, *ALL* of these fears and
insecure feelings are created by the drug itself and all of the
brainwashing since birth. Once all of the brainwashing is removed
and you purge the poison from your body all of the fears are
immediately destroyed. You never had these fears before you
started taking the drug and you won't have them again after you
stop, it's only drinkers that have these fears.

I now no longer have these fears. I am now physically and mentally free from the slavery of drug addiction. I once again have the true courage, true confidence, true relaxation, and true happiness that I was trying to get by having a drink! The drug had destroyed me for so long that I didn't realise that the only reason why I was having that drink was because of what the last drink had done to me. I was the mouse yet I thought I was a *true*man!

The advantages of not drinking could fill another book, as I have said the difference is like another world. More money, fitter, healthier, more energetic, more courageous, more self confidence, better able to relax, more self respect, a clear head, mentally and physically vibrant, happier, better love life!, more joy, more fun, more time, in short a much, much, much healthier and happier life. Free from *having* to exercise control over. TRULY FREE!

This is something organisations like AA believe is not only hard to achieve, but impossible. Yes according to them you can stop drinking, but instead of true freedom, the best you can expect is a life in ...

23

'Recovery'

You may or may not have heard about 'alcoholics' who stop drinking being in "recovery" for the rest of their lives. This, apparently, is one of the symptoms of being an alcoholic. One of the many books I read about alcohol was 'The Joy Of Being Sober' written by a man called Jack Mummy. He states quite categorically that you are different to everyone else, that you have inherited your 'disease' from your family and that alcoholism is in your genes. He also states throughout his book that the recovery process is hard, long and oh yes, it NEVER ends! He tells you this at the very start of the book! To be fair, Mr Mummy should have been done under the Trade's Description Act for calling it 'The *JOY* of being sober', it sounds a riot from the start, doesn't it?

Incidentally this wasn't the only book that referred to this 'recovery' symptom, in fact all the books on alcohol do.

How long does it take to fully recover anyway? Well here's the problem, apparently you *never* can. You can only expect to achieve a *satisfactory* way of life, taking each day as it comes. According to the leading experts in alcoholism, that is. So why can't you ever recover? It is because there is apparently no cure for this disease. But when you confront these 'experts' and ask them what disease are they talking about, they simply say *alcoholism*. When I ask them to explain what the cause of the disease is, they literally say *"The answer is not clear. But once you have the disease there is no cure, maybe once we can establish the cause we can begin finding a cure"* Find the cause! HELLLOOOO IS THERE ANYBODY HOME???? What are 'they' talking about? Do you really have to have a B.A. Honours in common sense to figure out that ALCOHOL is the cause of the disease? If somebody takes heroin on a regular basis or smokes cigarettes, do we say that the answer is not clear? Do we say that we do not know what the cause is? Of course it's clear, very clear!

The actual chemical addiction to alcohol is a disease in itself, which only gets worse and worse. That I agree with, if you want to call the disease *alcoholism* then fine, but the disease can only get worse while you are *still* taking the drug. The disease can also only be there whilst you are taking the drug. The disease ends the second you stop taking the drug! The disease is the drug!!!!

The 'recovery' process takes place all of the time when you ***are*** drinking alcohol, not when you are not. All of the disease has completely gone the very second you purge it from your mind and body. What is so difficult to understand about that?

They say that you are never really cured but in 'recovery' for the rest of your life. This is because if you have just one drink then it will start the 'disease' off again. But if you cannot be cured in the first place, then you must still have the disease even when you are not taking it, so how can it start again if you have a drink? How can something start again if apparently it could *never* be stopped in the first place? Even the expert's own arguments don't make sense. By that rationale, then every person on the planet was born with a disease called 'Heroinism'. If you were to start taking Heroin, then the chances are you will want to take more and more. It would destroy you mentally and physically and affect every area of your life. But please remember that if the drug takes hold it's not actually the drug that is the problem, it's you. The problem lies in the fact that you were born with this disease called Heroinism! Who in their right mind would believe such RUBBISH?

This recovery nonsense has NOTHING whatsoever to do with people's genetic makeup, character, or personality. It is simply mental deprivation because they believe that they are missing out on a genuine pleasure or genuine crutch. I hate to simplify it, but it really is simple!

Can you imagine somebody falling into quicksand, and after they were rescued the person who saved them saying,

"Now I am afraid to tell you that you are not truly free. You are now in 'recovery' from quicksand which will last for the rest of your life. It is not going to be easy as you will always want to jump back in. You will have a constant battle with yourself everyday for the rest of your life. But you must understand that you are not able to jump back in for if you do you will probably sink and die. You must make a vow to yourself that you are going to stay on dry ground for one day. Just one day – today! Take each day as it comes. But always remember once a quicksand sinker always a quicksand sinker!"

"But that will mean spending the rest of my life wishing that I could jump in quicksand with the knowledge that it will destroy me if I do. I feel in a no win situation. Does quicksand do this to everybody who jumps in?"

"No I am sorry to say <u>you</u> are the problem, not the quicksand. It is in your genetic make up, you were born a quicksand sinker"!!!!!

Perhaps this sounds a little stupid, but then so is the whole business of 'Recovery'. Maybe you are thinking, "why would you go through the rest of your life wanting to jump back in the quicksand when you <u>know</u> what it is like and have already been pulled free?" Very good question! But why would you want to inflict a disease upon yourself after you have already been cured of that disease? Why would anybody want to have a disease?

This 'recovery' is no more and no less than the 'willpower method' of trying to come off any drug. With other drugs it's called 'willpower', with alcohol it's called 'Recovery'. Why? Because we have been so brainwashed and conditioned to believe that the imbibing of alcohol is 'normal'. The people who cannot control their intake are not 'NORMAL'! So the only logical thing to say is that they have a disease. But as I have illustrated, there is no such thing as a normal drinker and nobody is <u>ever</u> in control, it's plain drug addiction. And drug addiction is a disease in itself. The *normal* drinker already has the disease, they just don't realise. The people who realise are called *alcoholics!*

The reason why the willpower method is so difficult is because the person stopping believes that they are making a genuine sacrifice. They strongly believe that they are giving up a genuine pleasure or crutch. So the second they say 'I am never going to drink again' they feel very deprived, not physically, but mentally. Think about it logically, even if the person doesn't drink again but believes that they are missing out on a pleasure or crutch, then the feeling of deprivation can be there, not just for that day, but for the rest of their lives. It is this and this alone; the waiting, the doubting and the uncertainty in the MIND, which is what people describe as 'recovery'. Is it any wonder that people who stop drinking after they are told they are not normal feel miserable?

When you actually confront the 'experts' about where this recovery takes place, where does it hurt? They don't actually know. They will go on and on about the D.T's, but even a lot of that is caused by mental deprivation and, besides, only lasts for a maximum of a few days if at all, so where is the problem after that? It's purely psychological, caused only by the feeling of deprivation, no more and no less.

This explains why there are some people who haven't had a drink in years, but are still pining away for a drink. In fact, unlike smoking where there are now millions of ex-smokers out there who don't miss them, with drink, not only do 90% of our own population drink the stuff and believe the illusions and brainwashing, but the ten per cent who do not drink are largely made up of whinging ex-drinkers!

I attended an A.A. meeting many years ago, which was a complete diatribe of sheer doom, gloom and misery. I must stress once more that A.A has helped many, many people and not all of their meetings are like this at all. Many can be funny and entertaining. But I also believe that there is no need to go to a building every week, state your name and complain about no longer *having* to drink. It would be a lot more understandable if they went somewhere every week and shouted at the tops of their voices "Isn't it great, I *don't have* to drink anymore!" The first person in this AA meeting stood up and said "I am John, I am an alcoholic". It turned out that he hadn't had a drink in

TWENTY YEARS! Twenty years and yet he still said that there isn't a day that goes by where he doesn't miss it. Miss what? There is simply nothing to miss. The pleasure or crutch of alcohol was a simple illusion based on the removal of natural fears and years upon years of advertising , conditioning and brainwashing. Think about this for a moment, TWENTY LONG YEARS and probably until the day he dies, that poor man has been and will continue –

MOPING FOR SOMETHING WHICH HE
HOPES HE WILL NEVER HAVE AGAIN!

Now that is a ludicrous and intolerable way to go through life isn't it? To be upset because you don't have something which you hope you won't have again! I recently read Frank Skinner's excellent and, as you'd expect, very funny autobiography Frank Skinner by Frank Skinner. In it there were a couple of things he said which really illustrates how some people never get mentally free from alcohol and how they are in a permanent state of recovery. When he's finished on stage, sometimes people ask him, 'were you happy with that', his reply, "No I haven't been happy since September 24 1986" – this is the last time he had an alcoholic drink. I must say I love Frank Skinner, I think he's really funny and sharper than Mr Sharp of Sharpsville (everyone to their own!), but after reading that I really felt sorry for him. He, like so many of the 'recovery gang', is in a no win situation. Does he spend the rest of his life wishing he could have something which he hopes he will never touch again? Or, does he give in to his own tantrum and become the mouse once again! What a choice! He has simply opted for what he believes is the lesser of two evils. This is called 'RECOVERY'. Can you imagine the scientist wanting to be the mouse? It would be even more ridiculous if the scientist was once a mouse himself and had already escaped!

People who go 'on the wagon' for just a couple of weeks also suffer from this mental deprivation, they're having to exercise immense willpower, discipline and control to 'give up' for just a couple of weeks. Are these people in 'recovery'? After all they are going through exactly the same thing as people in A.A. are going through – MENTAL

DEPRIVATION! But they cann... would be seen as an 'alcoholic', ... to admit for the first time that alco... they are simply HOOKED!

I have repeatedly emphasised throu... EASY to stop drinking and, more importa... for the rest of your life. People only disbeli... brainwashing largely perpetuated by other pe... stop, or by watching others who tried to stop b... wrong way. This gives the impression that it's difi... achieve freedom. There are, after all, whinging ex-... because they have a disease for which they can't be c... ...u have seen people 'on the wagon' for two weeks and every day they are telling you that they haven't had a drink for x amount of days. They are, at the same time, opting out of life by saying they would love to come out, but are not drinking at the moment. This simply perpetuates the false belief that people cannot enjoy themselves the same way without a drink. You have seen people who are told they cannot drink just for ONE evening because they have to drive and you have heard them say that the evening was pretty lousy because of it. You may have also been through this yourself, so your mind thinks if that is what it's like for a DAY, then what the hell will it be like FOREVER? If you have been conditioned to believe that you are what society describes as an alcoholic, then you begin your attempt to stop with the knowledge that you will NEVER BE FREE. Isn't that at the root of many of the fears that keep people hooked on alcohol? This fear has been perpetuated by society as a whole, the fear that you can never truly get free. The fear that you will always be missing out. No wonder people don't start off with a feeling of excitement, elation and freedom. We have been so brainwashed to believe that we can never get free, that it is not normal to be sober, that we *begin* our attempt to stop drinking with a feeling of doom and gloom, as if we have just made a genuine sacrifice. Instead of feeling elated, liberated, and joyous at the knowledge that we have just freed ourselves from one of the worst slavery's we will ever suffer from. That we have just stopped a progressive disease in it's tracks and will never have to suffer again.

...is the end of nothing more than a disease.
...yway? To simplify, it is where the person who
...ohol then puts themselves into a tantrum like a child not
...to have a toy. The theory is that if you suffer the misery of the
...ntrum for long enough then time will make things better and the
craving for alcohol will eventually go.

Let me ask a question – at what point did Nelson Mandela realise that he was free from his slavery? At what point was he free, never to return, ever again? Was it a year after he was released from that prison? A few months after? A week? A day? Or was it the very SECOND he was released from prison?

It was, of course, the very second he was let out, the very second he stepped outside to FREEDOM. Do you think that he ever gets a 'craving' to go back in? No, he knew for certain that he was free the moment he stepped out. But at what point can the poor ex-drinker say "have you heard the news, I've done it, I'm FREE, I NEVER have to drink alcohol ever again, isn't it marvellous!" At what point can they become elated that they are free? At what point will the craving go? The answer is NEVER, not while they still believe that they are making a GENUINE sacrifice.

I accept that in order to get free from any disease you *have* to realise that you have the disease, but it's just as important to realise when you don't have it any more. There is nothing sadder than a person who has freed themselves from a slavery, an addiction, a disease, but has no idea that they have.

The problem is that all of society is giving you the impression that you have indeed made a genuine sacrifice – that **you** will be the one who is missing out. So when people stop drinking they don't start off with a feeling of celebration that they have freed themselves of an awful addiction, but with a feeling of doom and gloom wondering WHEN they WILL fail! If the poor alcohol addict believes that they can never get free, then they NEVER will be free. Even if they don't drink for the rest of their lives, they will simply be waiting to see whether or not they fail. To be fair the rest of your life is an awfully long time to have to wait to see, and even then you don't find out, because once you are dead nobody sends you a congratulations card saying "Oh by the way you were free, you _did_ stop drinking you know"!

The trauma that the ex-drinker is going through when they stop is NOT caused by the awful physical pain of the drug leaving their body, or by anything in their genes, but the feeling of MENTAL DEPRIVATION! It is just like a child being told that it cannot have a toy. Our theory is that if we suffer the misery of this mental tantrum for long enough then eventually we might be able to reach the stage where we can say "I've done it I'm free". However, true freedom is impossible if you do that. The tantrum will be there forever to some degree while you believe you have made a sacrifice. As I have repeatedly emphasised, unless ALL of the brainwashing is removed, the feeling of deprivation can be there for the rest of their lives. This is NOT 'recovery' or 'remission' from a disease, it's mental deprivation just like a child being deprived of a toy. It is simply the feeling of 'missing out', no more and no less.

But what is there to be deprived of? What does alcohol do for you or anybody for that matter? The answer is absolutely NOTHING. It's all just one massive confidence trick. I stopped for three months once and whinged permanently. I look back now and see that it was all unnecessary as I was moping around for something that did not exist!

In order to succeed it must be clear in your mind that nobody is ever born an alcohol addict anymore than anyone is born a coffee drinker, or Mars bar eater for that matter. There is only one reason why people get hooked on alcohol and that is the brainwashing, or to put it another way .....

24

The Advertising

 There are only two kinds of advertising that get us hooked in the first place, or that keep people pining for a drink after they have stopped. They are:

1. The direct and commercial advertising
2. Other drinkers

Let's not underestimate the power of advertising, it works! That is why the alcohol industry spends £200M every year advertising their drug in the U.K. alone.

If the drug was launched today, nobody would go near it. Alcohol would never be legal, that's for sure. If you believe that you would be drinking alcohol without the influence of advertising and other drinkers, then imagine visiting another country which knows absolutely nothing about alcohol, and trying to sell the stuff to them. It would not be so much difficult as damn near IMPOSSIBLE!

If you tried to sell alcohol today to people who have never seen it you couldn't. It would be virtually impossible, it would just sound too ridiculous. It is extremely unlikely that anyone would consciously choose to take this product. Which is my point exactly, nobody is drinking out of *choice*, they *have* to or they are miserable and cannot cope, that is why the thought of stopping drinking permanently sends people into a panic. But why should it? I said at the start of this book that I would like you to open your mind, I would like you to continue to do so and to let me now try and persuade you to take this brand new drug that I have just been handed. Forget about alcohol for a second, this is a new drug. Think about it along the same lines as heroin or crack. I will firstly give you a complete list of all the disadvantages of taking this drug, then a very comprehensive list of all the advantages of taking it.

Finally, I will pose a question which I would like you to answer honestly.

First of all the disadvantages:

The drug comes in a liquid form which is the result of a process of decay.
It tastes disgusting.
It is also very addictive and the chances are that you will remain
    hooked for the rest of your life.
It will cost you at least one hundred thousand pounds in your lifetime.
It is a powerful poison.
Every fix will destroy thousands of your brain cells.
It will dehydrate your body so much that the day after imbibing it your
    brain will be smaller than the day before!
It will dull all of your senses.
It will stupefy you.
You will not be able to hold normal conversations.
It will slow down all of your reactions.
It will impair your ability to communicate efficiently and effectively.
It will slur your speech.
It will remove your natural fears making you vulnerable and
    completely unprotected. The drug will remove the safety check
    point between your brain and your mouth, and whatever comes into
    your head, no matter how stupid, offensive, obnoxious, aggressive,
    rude or outrageous, you will blurt out.
Because you have no natural protection, it will give you the illusion
    that you are now, more confident and more courageous.

Once you have suffered the illusion you will become completely
dependent on the drug and will not be able to enjoy yourself
without it.

Your body will quickly build up an immunity and tolerance to the drug,
so you will need more and more to get the same illusionary effect.

The more you take, the more it drags you down, the more it drags you
down the more you take.

It will destroy your courage.

It will undermine your confidence.

It will take away your self respect.

It will make you its slave for life.

You will reach the stage where it drags you down so much that you will
end up despising yourself for being a slave to something that you
will eventually hate.

I should also warn you that the first time you take it you will probably
be physically sick as it is so poisonous the body must get rid of it as
quickly as it can, otherwise you would die.

The drug in itself is a powerful anaesthetic, which means that it will
make you fall asleep. If you are lucky that is, chances are that you
will want to close your eyes, the room will spin when you do making
you feel sick, so you will want to keep your eyes open but will be
unable to because the drug has made you sleepy!

When you wake up from your ordeal your head will be pounding and
you will have one of the worst headaches you will ever suffer from.
This is caused by your blood trying to pump through a dehydrated
brain.

Your whole body will feel as if you have just been run over by a truck.

It will take *at least* three days for the effects of the drug to wear off!

Those are the disadvantages of taking this new drug, now for the
advantages:

What will it genuinely do for you?

NOTHING: NOTHING AT ALL.

The question is – Would you like some of this new drug? How much money would you pay me for it? Would anyone buy that drug?

Unfortunately, this wasn't how alcohol was advertised when I was growing up, it still isn't today and never will be. Why not? Why will it never be advertised as it actually is? Because alcohol represents a multi-trillion pound industry throughout the world. The bottom line is that they want your money. Alcohol is the last 'recreational' drug that is still legally allowed to be advertised on television and consequently they do it all the time. The majority of sporting events are sponsored by the alcohol giants, there are huge billboards everywhere promoting the drug. You will see glossy magazines with every other page a full page ad for alcohol. The advertisements themselves are images of 'coolness' or 'one of the lads' for beer, sophistication for wine or business executive types for scotch. You must wake up to all this bollocks, it's all simply intended to *keep* you hooked on a drug from which trillions are earned. The government won't stop the advertising either, it's big business for them too. Our own government earns TEN BILLION pounds a year profit, from a drug which is known to kill 40,000 people every year and destroys hundreds of thousands of lives at the same time.

Every television programme, film and even plays depict alcohol as a social pastime, constantly perpetuating the illusion that alcohol gives courage, confidence, relaxation and happiness. The truth behind the drug is *never* advertised, even in pubs like "The Rovers Return" and The "Queen Vic", nobody ever gets drunk! If you think about it, soap characters spend every lunchtime and every evening in the pub and yet nobody ever gets drunk. In fact if you were hooked, of all the pubs in the world, these are the three you would do your utmost to avoid! When somebody in these soaps does get drunk, they are seen as alcoholics and told to leave the pub. It is exactly the same in real life. Huge amounts of money are spent advertising alcohol, and most pubs and clubs will try and tempt you with "Happy Hours" and similar offers. The minute you get drunk, however, you will be thrown out for taking up their "offers". They will sell you a drug, which will stupefy you, make you act irrationally or in an obnoxious and violent manner.

This drug that will compel you to have more and more, yet the minute it takes effect, they want you out of their establishment. What hypocrites!

And how do these people in soap operas afford to drink from morning till night? Many of them are unemployed, so the "soap pubs" must be the cheapest in the world. After all it is a very expensive drug. All this subconscious advertising has a powerful effect on us, whether we are aware of it or not. We see images every day that it is 'normal', and 'natural' to drink every lunchtime and every evening, We become immune to the fact that it is completely unnatural to destroy our brain cells, courage and confidence on a weekly if not daily basis. We consequently end up strongly believing that it's normal to drink.

IT IS NOT NORMAL OR NATURAL TO IMBIBE ALCOHOL!

Alcohol is even advertised as a sexual aid. The advertising suggests that your love life will be enhanced with alcohol, 'just add the vodka' said one campaign in which it showed two girls getting well let's say very close. We are also bombarded by images of the 'fine' bottle of wine, open fire, nice music and sweet lovemaking. This might be the case *without* the alcohol, at least you would remember everything. At least you would feel every touch, each sensation, each moment. But "reality" with alcohol is anything but reality most of the time. Alcohol dulls ALL of your senses, so you cannot feel anything anyway. Too much of the stuff and men particularly know all too well what can happen, it isn't called "brewers droop" for nothing. The only 'stiff one' you can fix is the drink! Sometimes all the scaffolding in the world won't keep it up! The opposite problem can happen too where your senses are blown so much that you cannot focus on what you are doing, you simply cannot reach a climax no matter how hard you try!

Although I hate to admit it, this book is about reality, not lies and advertising and, I can honestly say, that I sometimes couldn't even remember having sex! Occasionally I would remember up to a certain point and the next thing I knew the alarm was going off. My mouth would feel like dirt and my breath would stink of alcohol at eight a.m., how romantic is that? It's funny how they don't advertise that to the kids when they are growing up. I was so trapped that I honestly thought that sex was better when I had had a few drinks. What rubbish! The best sex, or love making, takes place when you are SOBER, clear-headed and above all, have all of your senses about you. Some people dispute this, but this is only because they were on alcohol virtually every time they made love, so they have simply forgotten how wonderful it can be when sober. Making love is a happy *situation*, it is not the drink. Think about it, would *you* rather make love to a drunk or a person who knows what they are doing?

Sport and alcohol now go together hand in hand, from beer or lager for football to champagne for tennis. In 'France 98' (the football "World Cup") 'Carling, who were the main sponsors of football in the U.K. at the time, put a St George's Cross on each can during the competition. The association they wanted drinkers to make was England = Carling! Such is the power of advertising, it worked. Alcohol drinking is frequently advertised as a rebellious thing to do, *'Go to the dark side'* one advertising slogan suggests. *'94.7% Good'* says another one. Advertisers are always challenging us to be different, to be a rebel, to say "sod it" to society, "let's live," or "I don't care". This wouldn't be too bad if alcohol did any of those things. Let's get something very clear, there is nothing *different* or *rebellious* about doing the same thing as NINETY PER CENT OF THE POPULATION! If you really want to be a rebel, or different, become a person who doesn't need to take alcohol to enjoy or cope with life.

Look at the way in which alcohol is advertised as refreshing. It is just lie after lie. There is one old ad that showed a world that has run out of water. The sun is blazing and H2O is the most sought after commodity in this world, so much so that dealing in water is big business in the underworld. The ad shows a 'hunky' man (of course, what else? not someone with a beer gut the size of the Napa valley) walking through this world where everyone is dying of thirst. He then goes into a building, climbs the stairs and there is a 'beautiful' woman (of course, what else?) pouring him a pint. It ends with the slogan *'In a world that is losing its head, a lager that doesn't.'* The lager might not 'lose its head', but if you drunk it, you would. You might not only lose your head but also your family, home, money, brain cells, self respect, courage, confidence, and in forty thousand cases in the U.K. every year, your life! If there were no water in the world the last thing you would do would be to drink alcohol, it would drain any fluid you did have out of your body. I could go on about all the commercial advertising, but there really is no need, you know exactly what I'm talking about. After all you are bombarded with it every minute of the day, it's everywhere. The message in all these adverts remains the same; 'our job is to keep you hooked and get your money'.

Whether you realised it or not, all of the advertising is there as an aid to keep you hooked and a desperate attempt for you to change your brand. They will change the shape of their bottles, their image, even give the same product different names to 're-brand' them to look like something new. But no matter how powerful this direct advertising, it didn't get us hooked in the first place. So what on earth persuades us to take this drug in the first place? Was it really a billboard ad for alcohol, which made you leap and want your first drink? No. It was one thing and one thing alone, the same thing that causes anybody to try any drug – the people who are already hooked on that drug, in other words, in the case of alcohol, it's …

25

Other Drinkers

 The alcohol industry spends literally billions of pounds throughout the world every year advertising their drug, and yet the biggest sales force they have pays them!

Alcohol addicts are the biggest sales force that the alcohol industry has. Even Jack Dee (English comedian) who has attended A.A. advertises alcohol on television.

Remember, when you stop drinking and break free from this slavery, keep it clearly in your mind that *every* drinker you meet works for the alcohol industry. They have no idea they do, but they do. Looking back, I know I certainly did, I played my part at recruiting new customers for the industry. I once tried very hard to get a friend of mine hooked. She had never drunk alcohol in her life and had no desire whatsoever to do so. However, due to the massive brainwashing, I couldn't understand why she didn't want to drink. I never understood how she could possibly enjoy herself without joining us for a drink. Every time we were out I would say *"Go on, have a drink. What's the matter with you? You really don't know what you are missing."* I used to even say what a shame you *don't* drink? You see when you are hooked on a drug it becomes a mystery to you how anybody can enjoy life without it. The mystery to me now is how on earth did I believe I was enjoying myself when I was hooked on the drug.

The sad reality is that 'other drinkers' really do not mind you stopping drinking…providing that you are miserable! If you are moping around, getting uptight, depressed and whinging for a drink they are fine, but if you happy about stopping, they hate it. This is because all drug addicts do not like to be reminded that they *need* a drug. And that is inadvertently exactly what you are doing to them by enjoying and coping easily with life without 'having' to drink. So be alert, their constant need to justify their drug taking can lead them to constantly try to get you hooked again. As I have already said, if you stop smoking you are hero, if you stop drinking you are seen as a FREAK!

They will say things like *"How are you finding it?" "How's it going?" "it's early days yet"* or the classic question: **"ARE YOU STILL NOT DRINKING?"**

Just to inform you so that you are more than equipped for these attitudes, you will be asked this question until the day you die. "Are you STILL not drinking?!" I was getting this question thrown at me all the time when I stopped. *"still off the sauce Jace?" "How long has it been now then?" "How are finding it?"* Finding what? What the hell was I supposed to be looking for? When somebody passes their driving test do you phone them up a week after they have already passed and say, *"Can you still drive?"* NO of course you don't! If you met Nelson Mandela would you ask him if he is still free and if he is missing prison life? No of course you wouldn't. But we have been so brainwashed and conditioned for so long that it is IMPOSSIBLE to stop drinking and be happy about it for the rest of your life, that everybody is simply waiting to see WHEN you will 'give in' to the temptation.

But you can only ever be tempted if you buy into the advertising that alcohol will provide you with a genuine benefit. If you are truly free you cannot give in to temptation because you will not be tempted. You can only have the possibility of 'giving in' to something, if you have 'given up' something. And that is the best part of all about stopping drinking, it turns out, that contrary to what we have been brainwashed to believe, there is absolutely NOTHING to give up. The very expression 'I've given up' implies a sacrifice. That is why people suffer even after they stop. They believe they have made a sacrifice and that they have 'given up' something worth having. You are not giving up anything worth having. You are curing yourself of a progressive disease, you are stopping an addiction. It is the people who are trying to advertise it to you (other drinkers) who are 'giving up' and making huge sacrifices. They are giving up their health, money, courage, confidence, and freedom. Whether they know it or not they are drug addicts and as such have a progressive disease. That is not something to envy, it is something to genuinely pity.

Other drinkers are without doubt the biggest sales force there is for alcohol. It is what got us hooked in the first place and it's only the belief that they are deriving some sort of genuine pleasure from alcohol that keeps people still craving a drink after they stop. The addicts themselves are constantly trying to justify why they drink. They will constantly tell you that *you* are missing out. The sad truth is that they are missing out. They instinctively know this and would love to be in your position – a happy non-drinker. Their disbelief that anybody can stop and not miss drinking keeps them asking questions. *"How are you finding not drinking?"* Well apart from the factual answer which will be *"fantastic thank you"*, you can always ask them how are they finding *having* to drink? The question "How are you finding *not* drinking" is ridiculous anyway. The real question should be "how is the drinking going? How are you finding the hangovers, the memory loss, the cost, the arguments, the lethargy, the slavery, the having to control etc; believe me they will soon end the subject. You will of course get the inevitable answers at times *"I don't get hangovers after drinking"*. That is really worrying. This means that they have simply built up such an immunity and tolerance to the drug that hangovers have become a way that they normally feel. They are so used to alcohol leaving the body that they think that this is normal! Or, of course it may be the case that they are simply lying like any other drug addict to try and justify their intake.

All alcohol addicts are always trying to justify why they *choose* to do it, especially if they are with somebody who has stopped drinking, who clearly doesn't miss it, and has no *need* for the drug anymore. The alcohol never changes only the excuses to justify their intake. If you ask a young kid why they are drinking they will say *"I enjoy drinking"*. They are lying right from the start. It's obvious to both parties that they are not actually enjoying it. Every time they take a sip they shudder, they get very stupefied, and feel like shit the next day. Some even vomit when they first take alcohol and they wish they were really having a lemonade anyway. But they have been conditioned to believe that it's not adult enough to drink lemonade anymore, so whilst in the learning process they will say *"I enjoy it"*. They are trying to justify their intake from the start and it never stops. If you ask the same youngster why they drink a few weeks later they will now say *"I like the taste"*. What they really mean is that they no longer find the same taste offensive. Ask them some time later and they will say *"It gives me courage, confidence, helps me to relax and makes me feel happy"*. So in just a few short months, the alcoholic drink has changed from something that made you feel dreadful and tasted awful, into something which, not only tastes good now, but is also a prop or a crutch.

It's blatantly obvious that the alcoholic drink itself hasn't changed, merely the youngster's perception of it.

All of our lives our reasons for drinking alcohol changes from one drink to the next to try and justify why we do it, but the real reason always remains the same 'alcohol addiction'. So be alert, all alcohol addicts will do this. They will say stupid things, which appear to be good, sound logical things to say on the surface, but in reality, are very pathetic. They are so scared of stopping themselves that when you achieve something that they think is out of their reach, they will try anything to get you back. You might say things like, *"have you heard the news, I don't need to drink anymore, I'm free"*. (After all it is worth voicing. It's not everyday you free yourself from a slavery and stop a disease in its tracks!) You will inevitably get more questions *"Well how long has it been? I wouldn't speak too soon, it is after all early days yet"*. What the hell has time got to do with it? Does it really matter how long you have been free, as long as you are free?

That is all 'recovery' is – counting the days waiting for something to happen. But waiting for what? The day you can say *"I've done it. I don't need to drink anymore. I'm free"* The truth is that you can say it from day one. And if you say it from day one then you are truly free from day one. If you do not say it on day one, then when are you going to say it?

Did Nelson Mandela get this nonsense when he was released from his captures? Did he hear people saying *"I wouldn't celebrate yet Nelson, it's only been a week!"* Time means nothing. How long is it since you passed your driving test? How many days exactly? You really don't know because it doesn't matter, you can drive and that's that. You don't take one day's driving at a time in case you crash! If somebody was pulled from quicksand, do you think for one second that they would be counting the days that they are *still* out? Do you believe that it would take a year to prove that they were free? Of course not. So there is no need whatsoever to count days when you stop drinking, it's meaningless and pointless. This is a very important part of the method. DO NOT COUNT DAYS WHEN YOU ARE FREE.

The second that you know you have consumed your last drink, you are free at that moment! This is without doubt the most bizarre prison in the world. It is the only prison where people count the days *after* they have been released!

But such is the nature of the alcohol confidence trick that drinkers will actually believe that *you* are missing out, this is why they will be baffled as to why you have stopped drinking altogether. Or, if you were seen as an 'alcoholic' in their eyes already, they will feel sorry for you because you 'can't' have a drink anymore. What they will not understand is that *they* are the ones that are missing out, and once fully understood, you will be feeling sorry for them! It becomes very easy to see that *they* are the ones who are being deprived. They are *having* to exercise control and are dependent on a drug. If you do not consume alcohol you are being deprived of **ABSOLUTELY NOTHING**.

Focus clearly the reality of the situation. No matter how long you have stopped for, it is the poor drinkers who are the ones ultimately missing out and being deprived. They are being deprived of their health, their money, their brain cells, their memory, their senses, their peace of mind, their courage, their confidence, and most of all, their physical and mental *freedom*. They are DRUG ADDICTS. You will be one of the first to truly see them for what they are. I doubt if you would envy a heroin addict – so why envy alcohol addicts?

THERE IS NOTHING TO ENVY, YET SO MUCH TO PITY

Always remember what got us all hooked in the first place – ALCOHOL ADDICTS! It is the drinker who convinced us that we were missing out in the first place. If I had the job of making somebody believe in Santa Claus, I would recruit a child to do it for me. What better person to convince somebody of an illusion than someone who honestly believes the illusion to be true? Don't forget the drinker themselves are being deluded. A part of them believes the illusions to be true. Never underestimate the power of 'other drinkers' and the huge amount of brainwashing which accompanies them. It seems that *everyone* drinks the stuff. From the down and out on the street to the president of the United States. We have been conditioned from birth to drink alcohol. Even your own parents may think that there is no harm in having a little glass of wine with a meal when you are TEN! They think "what's wrong with a little glass of wine?" That is the almost the same as saying 'what's wrong with a little Heroin!' They are both drugs, they are both addictive and they both destroy lives. The only difference is that one is seen clearly for what it is and is not being pushed on every television programme or film as a sociable, stress relieving happy pill, and the other one constantly is. You would never envy a heroin addict so why envy drinkers after you stop and have your freedom back? It would be ridiculous to envy something that you don't actually want to be – a drinker. Remember, the only difference between heroin and alcohol is that one is legal. One is seen for what it actually is, the other is seen from an addict's perspective.

The main problem with alcohol is that, unlike heroin, the addiction is so subtle that many people have lived and died without ever realising that they were addicts. Unfortunately, if they are aware of the dependency they have to block it from their minds for fear they might have an incurable disease and have to turn into a social recluse! You know, that mystical one known as *alcoholism*. So they continue to try to justify their intake with deceit and lies, not only to other people, but also to themselves, just like any other DRUG ADDICT. However, do not let this cloud the issue. No matter what drinkers believe, regardless of *anything* they say, the truth is that they are obviously hooked. This is not me being arrogant, it is factual. They may well not even realise they are trapped, but they are. As such it means that they are suffering from drug addiction and they do have a disease which, slowly but surely, will only get worse and worse. It means that they are *having* to exercise control, which means they are being controlled. Always keep it clear in your mind that drinkers are never in *true* control. It is a form of self imposed torture to try and control a drug. The drug *always* ultimately controls its victims. The drug dictates to the addict, not the other way around. This is the main reason why people remain hooked, or what gets them hooked again. They believe they can control alcohol. I stopped for three months and one of my reasons for having a drink again was that it could do no harm as I could now control it. But that was the problem. Why would you want to try and gain control of something that does NOTHING for you? Why would you want to try and control a disease instead of just not having the disease? Why would you want to spend the rest of your one and only life using willpower and discipline trying to keep in control of a drug that does absolutely nothing for you whatsoever? The only time you would ever want to control it is if you thought that YOU were missing out on a genuine pleasure. Which is exactly what got us all hooked in the first place. Remember, the only reason we had our first drink was because we felt as though we were missing out. The brainwashing since birth and our role models convinced us that we could have more fun by imbibing alcohol. It was 'other drinkers' that fooled us to begin with, and it is only the belief that 'other drinkers' are getting some benefit from alcohol that can possibly get you hooked again.

Would you envy someone with HIV even if you knew that it wouldn't develop into full blown AIDS for another twenty five years? You would never envy somebody with a disease that will probably lead to an even worse disease. You would never envy them, only pity them.

Above all you must realise that ALL drinkers are in the 'alcohol trap' whether they realise it or not. They are all simply at different stages of this progressive disease, that's all. People sometimes say to me *"If they don't know that they are hooked and in a trap, then surely it doesn't matter if they drink, their ignorance is bliss"*. Imagine that you were in quicksand, but didn't understand the nature of quicksand. Let us assume that you even believed that you were having fun playing in the quicksand. If I came along and pulled you out without your consent, you would be annoyed and upset that I had spoilt your fun. You would immediately want to jump back in. But if I explained the nature of quicksand and pointed out that you were in fact trapped and there was only one direction which was down, with no chance of escape, would you still want to jump back in? Do you think for one second that you would EVER go back in there again? Do you think for one moment that you would feel deprived even if at the time you thought you were having fun in there? Would you **ENVY** other people slowly sinking in the sand, even if they were only up to their waist? Or would you pity them and try to help them out? Of course you would want to help them, but they wouldn't want your help. They would only ask for your help when they began to realise that they were trapped, and not until then.

Imagine being in a position where you are sinking in quicksand and you finally realise what is happening. You call for help. But instead of help you are told that *you* are different. You are told that ninety percent of the population is in quicksand too, but they are fine and normal. They are not sinking at all, it's YOU with the problem. YOU just can't handle quicksand and if you seek help to get out, you will be made a social outcast forever because you have a disease for which there is no cure and you will be miserable and depressed for the rest of your life because you can't do something that everybody else can!

The problem is that if you were aware that you were sinking then you would think twice about seeking help (if that's what you thought would happen to you.) This is what frustrates me so much. We are in a position where alcohol addicts feel too ashamed to seek help because they have been taught if they need help *they* are different. Alcohol creates fear as it is, the last thing the drinker needs is the additional fear of being made to feel weak and disease ridden for life!

Going back to the quicksand, if you knew that the sinking had nothing to do with you, but that the nature of quicksand was to pull you under and you could see that *everybody* was sinking, you would jump for joy because you were free. The last thing you would ever do would be to envy people who are still sinking.

So this point must be clear, **never** envy 'other drinkers', there is nothing to envy. Remember that point, no matter how long you have stopped for. The facts about drinking alcohol *never* change, only their relevance to you. Once you purge the poison from your mind and body completely, you see clearly that there is nothing to miss. People go through a mourning process when they stop drinking, rather like mourning the loss of a close friend. They feel a sense of loss. The truth is that drinkers are the ones who are losing and missing out. Do not envy them, pity them. They need your pity.

This is one of the key instructions to life long success. Drinkers are in a trap that, in reality, they would dearly love to get free from too. I have realised since stopping drinking, that *all* alcohol addicts actually envy _me_! Not for any other reason than I am free. They would love to be in a position where they could enjoy and cope with life without the dependency on alcohol. The only thing stopping them is fear. The fear of quitting. The same fears that I had for years. Make a point of observing drinkers. Notice how *they* just won't let the subject lie when they realise that you genuinely do not *need* alcohol any more. Notice how, at the end of an evening, they have gained *nothing* by drinking. Notice how they are **constantly** telling you that they are in control, **constantly** telling you how little they need to drink, and permanently trying to justify why they are having that 'one' at the moment. What you must realise, is that no matter what they say, they would love to be like YOU, free from an awful slavery.

ALL DRUG ADDICTS LIE, EVEN TO THEMSELVES!

When they see that you are happy and cheerful about the fact that you don't *need* to drink anymore, they will think that you are super human, the fact is that you *feel* super human yourself! After all, they would expect you to whinge, at least a little! It is only whinging ex-drinkers that perpetuate the illusion that it is a life long struggle and disease, and that it is impossible to get truly free.

So do not envy drinkers, realise the truth, they will be envying you. This is not a trick way of looking at it, but a FACTUAL way. Every drinker you meet will secretly envy you. I say secretly, because they are not allowed to admit that they do, otherwise it will immediately confirm that they are not in control. So they have to keep up the pretence and lies for as long as possible and say over and over again "I'm in control. I don't have a problem". They say this so much that they believe it. Remember true control is when you no longer have to exercise control. No drug addict likes taking their drug alone. When I say "alone" I do not mean by themselves, I mean when they are with other people who are not taking the drug 'with them'. This is when they sense that they are really alone (hence the question *are you going to join me?*) So they will say anything to get you to have a drink again, anything to make you 'join them' once again. Anything to get you hooked. They will never see it that way as most have no idea that they are hooked themselves. But they will, whether conscious or subconscious, be trying to sell you the drug. Not because they are malicious people who want to inflict you with a disease again, but because they actually believe in the illusions and have no idea that it is a disease.

Drinkers get people hooked, get that clear. For what better person to sell you an illusion than the person who believes that it is real? This I believe is the saddest thing about this addiction, people honestly think that they are deriving some genuine pleasure from alcohol and that they are in full control. Because they don't drink in the morning, they have been taught to believe that it's perfectly normal to drink at any other time.

IT IS NOT *NORMAL* TO INFLICT YOURSELF WITH A DISEASE.

I have already illustrated that you can never be in control of a drug and that the natural tendency of any drug is to take more and more, so how come there seems to be so many people who can ......

26

Take It Or Leave It

 This is the cleverest part of the trap. This is what really confuses everyone. If it's the same trap for everyone then why do we not all sink at the same rate? Why can some people take it or leave it and others can't?

This is without doubt the biggest illusion of all when it comes to alcohol, the mass illusion that people can take it or leave it. This is why there is a divide with this drug, *normal* vs. *alcoholic*. The truth is that the natural tendency is to take more and more of the drug, to keep on hitting the button (mouse in cage). However, unlike the mouse we do have a higher consciousness and there is one main reason why some people do not increase their intake and become what society would describe as an alcoholic and that is:–

RESTRICTIONS!

Think about it, the only reason why people do not drink more and more is because they are forced not to drink either by themselves or society in general. It is only restrictions which prevent people from becoming what society describes as alcoholics any sooner. And there are so many restrictions when you think about it, whether it's money, health, effects on the family, because you are driving, because you have to work, fear you will be judged by others, fear you'll turn into an alcoholic, then there are your children, social stigma, not physically being capable of coping with the poison, or because you actually hate being drunk yourself!

Money plays a major role in restricting people's intake of the drug. After all it is a very expensive drug. Some people simply do not have enough money to increase their intake, so they will try and gear their intake according to what's in their pocket. After all they are already going to spend £100,000 on the drug as it is. It seems funny that the whole thing comes full circle as it were. People at the start of the trap drink cheap alcohol like cider and people at the end drink cheap alcoholic drinks like cider! I reached the stage where I was drinking 'Tennants Super' and 'Special Brew'. Did I really think they were *superior* brands, or was I simply trying to get more alcohol for less money? This is why people go from beer to spirits, to get more alcohol for less money. Like all drugs, your body builds up an immunity to the drug so you need more and more to try and do what it did before. To get the extra in, it becomes easier and cheaper overall to drink spirits. The fact is that many people cannot afford to increase their intake so they have no choice but to hold it at some kind of level. Obviously even this goes out of the window the further into the trap you get and you reach the stage where you will do without food, family and friends to get drink!

Health is another major restriction, whether drinkers like it or not, the same drug that they think gives them pleasure, also just happens to be the number two killer drug in Western society! Just because it's not really talked about doesn't change the reality. I used to have to watch my drinking due to my weight (my beer gut if you will). Alcohol really does 'weigh' you down in every way.

Looking back and seeing it now from an outside view, when I *was* drinking I had to exercise willpower and discipline to some degree everyday. These disciplines were enforced on me most of the time, however the confidence trick was so subtle that I thought I was choosing not to drink, not that I simply couldn't even if I wanted to. There were just so many restrictions preventing me from drinking more and more. When I had no job and was living in a squat in south

London, I drank as much as my pocket would allow. When I had a job I drank as much as my work would allow. As much as the relationship would allow, etc.. And isn't this really true for you? Do you find that sometimes you simply cannot drink even when you want to? Do you find that if you haven't got to work or you are on holiday or not driving that you drink a lot more than if you are not *having* to restrict yourself? If you are honest you know that you do! All drinkers do. And if you don't, then chances are you are already on skid row, which would mean that you are still having to discipline yourself anyway due to cost!

If alcohol really did all the things that we all believe it does, then our natural tendency would be to have more courage, confidence, and happiness first thing in the morning. Why delay having joy and happiness, why not have it as soon as we wake up?

The reality is that we know instinctively that it's all lies, for if you had a drink in the morning you would have no life! Those drinkers who do drink first thing in the morning no longer even suffer the illusion of enjoyment. They feel miserable when they are drinking and miserable when they aren't!

Smokers have a cigarette first thing in the morning and still function. It is seen as *abnormal* for a smoker not to smoke in the morning. Alcohol, however, is mind altering, so you *have* to discipline yourself. Many addicts won't even go out some nights because they have work in the morning. Some addicts will go all week without a drink because of restrictions, whether it's their work, their children, having to drive, being worried about their health, their money, their business or whatever. They have no choice but not to drink and many simply accept it and crack on with their lives and are perfectly happy in doing so, (which proves that the physical withdrawal is not the problem) but as soon as the weekend comes and they have no restrictions, they take the drug like there is no tomorrow; they tend to binge drink. They spend all week looking forward to when they can take their drug without having to restrict themselves, (providing they're not driving of course!). Then they find that they forget and, ultimately, lose the very weekend they were looking forward to because of the drug they were looking forward to taking! I know first hand because I used to do exactly that.

How many people do you know that say they only drink 'every now and then' but go mad either on holiday or at weekends? Holidays are the time when you see the alcohol addict in their true light. Many drinkers who wouldn't normally touch a drop during the day due to restrictions (and actually judge other people that do), are now having a pint on the beach at 10am! That is if they are up that early, chances are they don't arrive on the beach until 1pm anyway due to the fact that they were so plastered the night before. Of course it's OK to drink at 1pm, it is perfectly *normal*. What they fail to realise is that they have only been up for an hour! But what the hell does time matter anyway? If you drink you drink. Do you think that you would look at a heroin addict differently if they said *"It's OK, I don't have my first 'hit' until 1pm, I don't need it first thing"*? Of course you wouldn't.

All drug addicts have to exercise control to some degree because of certain restrictions. The real slavery is this constant need to control. And the biggest gain you will get from being totally free, is literally that, your freedom. If you are being controlled to any degree then you are not free. If you are dependent on any substance then you are not free. If you have to look at your watch to see if you can have a drink, then you are not free. If you are having to hold it at a certain level because of restrictions, then you are not free. If you are timing your drinks, then you are not free. And all drug addicts lie, including drinkers. *"I only have one glass a day"*. What they fail to tell you is that it's a pint of scotch!

Understand that there are only two reasons why people do not become heavy drinkers:

1. They are not physically strong enough to cope with that amount of poison at once; and
2. They have more restrictions in their lives which prevents the natural increase.

All drinkers can turn into heavy drinkers in an instant. It only takes one really bad moment in life and WHAM! They no longer have the strength or the inclination to control and the flood gates open.

Yes but what about ....

27

Binge Drinkers

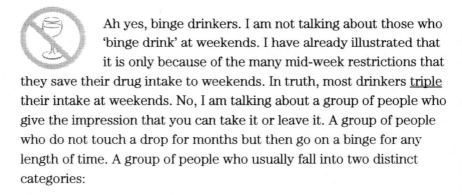 Ah yes, binge drinkers. I am not talking about those who 'binge drink' at weekends. I have already illustrated that it is only because of the many mid-week restrictions that they save their drug intake to weekends. In truth, most drinkers <u>triple</u> their intake at weekends. No, I am talking about a group of people who give the impression that you can take it or leave it. A group of people who do not touch a drop for months but then go on a binge for any length of time. A group of people who usually fall into two distinct categories:

1. Those who really do not think that alcohol has any benefit and do not miss alcohol when they are not drinking.
2. Those who really do miss alcohol when they are not drinking and are in a sense simply 'on the wagon'.

In both cases when they are drinking, they *really are* drinking. All the restrictions in the world would not stop them drinking. From morning till night they *have* to drink, there are no half measures. They just continue to 'hit the button' and sod the consequences.

The first category are the people who when they are not drinking genuinely do not miss alcohol at all. They can actually see it for what it is when they are off the booze and wouldn't let you give them the stuff. The problem is that they do believe one of the illusions – it helps to block the mind from stress. They binge drink as a way to cut off from reality. Reality has simply become too much and they cannot take it any more. So it's either join the foreign legion or go on a binge. If heroin were legal they would probably use that to block out life instead. In a sense it has nothing to do with alcohol addiction, it could be anything to block their minds. They choose alcohol because it does not require a prescription, it is legal and it is readily available from almost anywhere. These people are not actually addicted to alcohol, they do not think that there is any pleasure in drinking, they simply think it will act as a catalyst to escapism. The problem is that because alcohol is a depressant it actually drags them down even further than they already were, giving them even more reason to want to escape! They wake up feeling even worse than they were already feeling the day before, so they drink more. The initial reason for wanting to block their mind is getting worse by the day because they haven't dealt with it, again causing an even greater need to block the mind. Many binge drinkers have destroyed everything they have worked for in a matter of weeks. One day they realise that the drinking is destroying their lives even more than the reason for wanting to block their minds in the first place! It dawns on them what they are doing and they realise that it simply has to stop. They make the decision to get on with their lives and quit drinking. These people are playing a dangerous game and if they believe it has one benefit, it won't take long before they believe all the illusions. The time they spend not drinking will decrease and the time they spend bingeing will increase. This type of drinker is rare, but does exist, which is why I have covered it in this book.

The second type of binge drinker is the most common. This is the "three months on, three months off" drinker. When they are *not* drinking they *are* missing it. They feel miserable and deprived without it, they feel as though they are missing out. However they do not say that they feel deprived to the listening public, in fact they openly judge everybody else who drinks and become real "holier than thou" ex-drinkers. (There is nothing worse!) They are *resisting* all the time, they are using discipline whenever they are not drinking and their entire thoughts are taken up with not drinking. Eventually something happens in their life where their resistance runs low and they do not have the mental power to resist any longer. They have now reached the 'dam' situation. This is where there is so much pressure put on the 'dam' wall from the water build up that when it starts to crumble, all the water comes crashing through and although the 'dam' *appeared* strong, it collapses within seconds. It is the same for the poor 'binge drinker'. The problem is that in order not to drink it requires them to use incredible control on a massive scale. So everyday pressure is building up and it simply takes one moment of stress or a big social gathering and WHAM! The walls have broken and they subconsciously try and make up for lost time. The need for the drug is caused by the drug, so the more they have initially, the more they will have the next day. When they are drinking they hate it and when they are not drinking they hate it. During the time spent not drinking they are simply 'ON THE WAGON' and if you are 'on the wagon' it means that you are not drinking AT THE MOMENT. If you go on the wagon then it is inevitable that you will come off it again.

The problem is that the poor drinker honestly believes that they have indeed fallen 'off the wagon' and the only way to solve this problem in their minds is to go back on the wagon again. Being on the wagon is not a great deal of fun either, so eventually it becomes easier to stay off the wagon even though that's painful to.

When binge drinkers are 'off the drink' or 'on the wagon' they also become "holier than thou" ex-drinkers. These are the sort of people who do something for years, stop, and then spend all their time judging people who do what they used to do. These people fall into two categories themselves:

1. The drinker who has stopped but is using willpower, discipline and permanent control not to drink. These people are the 'recovery mob', still missing it they believe that they have made a genuine sacrifice. However they do not wish to say this because they would appear weak-willed, so they opt for the 'holier than thou' approach.

2. The people who have NEVER drunk alcohol. When I say never, I mean those who had their first drink, and hated it so much that they just were not willing to go through the learning process. After all it's not easy to get over the foul taste and awful effects that the first drink produces. Virtually everybody has tried alcohol at least once in their lives. These are NON-DRINKERS. They have never been hooked because they have NEVER suffered any of the illusions that the drug creates. These people plainly and simply cannot see why anybody drinks and because of this can appear on the surface to be somewhat self-righteous. However, their attitude is more than understandable and is exactly the same as *your* attitude to people who take heroin, you just think WHY? What they do not realise is that the poor drinker is under the control of a very clever confidence trick, if they did realise this they would not be so quick to judge. If people knew how desperately heroin addicts wanted to stop, they also wouldn't be so quick to judge them either.

What is so wonderful about this method to stop drinking is that you will not turn into a 'holier than thou' ex-drinker. In reality, once you fully understand the alcohol trap (as you will by the time you finish this book), you will genuinely feel sorry for those people left who still *have* to drink and are gradually sinking further and further down. You certainly will not become judgmental towards those around you who are still in the trap, don't forget you were once there yourself.

I have said that it is only fear that keeps people hooked and so powerful are these fears that the thought of stopping altogether is just too much, drinkers think that it will be easier to just ....

28

Cut Down

 NO! NO! NO! NO! Have I repeated that enough? Cutting down is what alcohol addicts do everyday of their lives. As I have just illustrated drinkers are permanently having to use willpower, discipline and control not to increase their intake.

Let me ask you a question, does dieting make food less precious or a **thousand** times more so? When I was drinking it was like being on an *alcohol diet* most of the time. When you are on food diet you have to exercise control and when you are dependent on alcohol you have to do the same. So I was either on an *alcohol diet* or forgetting the diet and bingeing because I just couldn't be bothered to control anymore.

You have been trying to 'cut down' all of your life, that is what this nonsense of 'going on the wagon' is all about. That is what ridiculous books like '*How To Give Up Alcohol For One Month*' are all about. When you have made a conscious decision to cut down in the past, did you enjoy the process? Did you have fun 'on the wagon' or were all your thoughts about when you could have your next drink? People end up wishing their lives away at such times.

This brings me back to Drink Line and their amazing and *effective* strategies to help reduce your drinking (or cut down). They go something like this:-

1. CHANGE YOUR ROUTINE – Perhaps start drinking later each time, or go out later than usual.

I am writing this with disbelief! I have read the first strategy given to help you to reduce your drinking a few times now, but cannot grasp the fact that adults apparently write this stuff! START DRINKING LATER? GO OUT LATER? Is this meant to be real advice? Constructive advice? Whenever I used to get into the pub late, my goal was to order as many drinks as I could before the bell struck for 'TIME'! I remember several times, waiting to go out to the pub, but having to wait for other people to get ready. I used to get very frustrated at waiting and pace up and down looking at my watch every five minutes, simply because I knew that we were missing valuable drinking time. If you have ever arrived in a pub late, do you drink less? Or do you simply order more drinks so that they are stacked around the table for fear that the bell could strike at any moment?

2. GIVE YOURSELF TIME BETWEEN DRINKS AND SET A GOAL OF ONE DRINK PER HOUR.

Do we really need this advice to be written down? This is what cutting down is all about and what alcohol addicts do most of the time anyway. As for this "setting yourself a goal of one drink per hour", have they no idea how alcohol works? Have they ever drunk alcohol themselves? After your second drink when you have 'the taste' your conscious mind has just been altered and you are in no position to stick to your "one drink an hour" nonsense. You simply say *"sod this for a game of soldiers"*. The chances are that there are many times when you do go out and have just one an hour, but who is timing this? The very second you say that you can ONLY have one an hour then you start timing. The drink then becomes the forbidden fruit once again. This makes it not less precious, but more so. The more you tell yourself you can't have, the more you will want to have. So in this situation you will be miserable trying to maintain control and feeling guilty and weak when you fail to achieve this.

3. DO SOMETHING WHILST YOU DRINK SUCH AS PLAY DARTS, BINGO OR DANCE.

This is the same advice they give for stopping altogether. It really amazes me that people can give out claptrap advice like this and are seen as leading *experts* in their field. If they only *remained* in a field we'd all benefit!

Go and play bingo! That's right, go and have a game of bingo, that will help you cut down on your drinking won't it? The last suggestion is the most pathetic by far. DANCE! How the hell is dancing going to reduce your alcohol intake? When you dance you get hot and THIRSTY so you have a drink. A drink which, will not quench your thirst but cause you to feel dehydrated. So when you dance again you will be even thirstier. They advise you to do this WHILST you are drinking, **dance whilst drinking?**

4. TRY LOW ALCOHOL AND NON ALCOHOL DRINKS – you may like them!

Well cover me in eggs and flour and bake me for thirty minutes, why didn't I think of that? In fact why didn't we all think of that? All we had to do was drink non alcoholic drinks!

5. HAVE SOMETHING TO EAT BEFORE YOU START DRINKING OR AT LEAST DRINK SOME MILK.

Does this make any sense whatsoever? How on earth is this pathetic piece of advice ever going to help you reduce your intake of alcohol? After you eat something or 'line your stomach' with milk, it doesn't stop you drinking does it? NO, quite the opposite in fact. The alcohol takes longer to reach the brain so you will feel as though you can drink as much as you like. The reality is that you drink more. I used to drink milk before going out sometimes so that I could drink *more*!

6. HAVE DAYS OFF FROM DRINKING!

Isn't this why we are asking their advice? We want to know how to do it and still feel happy.

7. KEEP A DRINK DIARY AND RECORD WHEN YOU DRANK, HOW MUCH YOU DRANK AND WHAT WAS THE SITUATION LEADING TO YOUR DECISION TO DRINK.

Do I even need to say a word on this one? 'Keep a drink diary'. NO CHANCE. I would either have been too drunk to remember how many I'd had, why, or what the situation was leading to the decision to drink, or far too hungover to care anyway. A drinks diary? I ask you, do you think these people were actually sober while writing this advice?

8. SIP YOUR DRINK RATHER THAN GULP IT DOWN AND PUT YOUR GLASS DOWN BETWEEN SIPS.

So sipping your drink rather than gulping it down will help to reduce your drinking? No, really!! But HOW do you stop gulping it down? That is the real question. That is why people are asking your advice, not so that people will state the obvious!

9. IF YOU ARE GOING TO DRINK, STICK TO ONE SESSION OF DRINKING DURING THE DAY.

So if you drink in the morning...DON'T STOP ALL DAY!

10. REWARD YOURSELF

OK, let's have a drink.....(oh shit wrong reward!) It's no good advising a drinker to reward themselves when they still believe that alcohol is a reward in itself.

The whole business of giving advice on reducing your intake or 'cutting down' is ridiculous anyway. This is because alcohol is a drug and you cannot control a drug, if you try the *need* will be greater.

Think about it, if you are one of these drinkers who perhaps has a couple in the evening and a skinful at the weekends, then you have probably gone for days or weeks, in the past without a drink and haven't been bothered by it. But the very second you tell yourself you **CAN'T**, you have the 'forbidden fruit' syndrome. And the reality is that drinkers on the whole are strong willed people and hate being told what to do by anybody else, including themselves. So when you say *I can't* drink, alcohol becomes a THOUSAND times more precious and you immediately feel miserable and deprived, even if you would normally find it easy to abstain for a few days. The reason why you now find it difficult is because you have told yourself that YOU CAN'T drink.

Get this very clear in your mind, when you stop drinking you CAN drink whenever you wish, just as I can whenever I wish. I just <u>don't</u> wish. I have no desire to drink ever again. You CAN after all take heroin whenever you wish, nobody is stopping you, so why don't you? Because you don't *want* to that's why. You CAN do whatever you want, the choice will be yours. You no longer have a choice if you do have a drink. Alcohol removes your freedom of genuine choice. All drugs do. You must understand that alcohol is not a hobby or a habit, and it is certainly not a genuine pleasure, it is drug addiction, NOTHING MORE AND NOTHING LESS.

Remember that the addiction is only psychological, if you tell yourself that YOU can't then you will feel deprived and miserable, the real question should be 'I *can* have a drink but what on earth would be the point, what would it do for me?' The answer will be crystal clear....NOTHING! There is just no point to drinking. Just saying the word *"can't"* or actually believing that you can't would be the only thing that could make it remotely difficult for you to stop drinking or remain free. Remember "can't" simply means;

Constant And Never-ending Torture

So why put yourself through a completely unnecessary mental torture? Especially when you will simply be saying that you can't have something that doesn't exist anyway! Something that you hope you will never have! Alcohol exists as a product, of course, and unfortunately will do so for many years to come, but all the things that you thought alcohol did for you do *not* exist. They are all illusions. And you were only *addicted* to the illusions.

Trying to cut down your intake simply means not being allowed to drink when you want to and having to exercise even more conscious control than before. The longer you suffer any aggravation the *more* marvellous it will appear to you when you eventually end it. If you are banging your head against a brick wall, the longer you are doing it the more pleasure you will get when you stop. But it's not pleasure, it's simply the ending of an aggravation. Why bang your head against the wall in the first place? Why drink? And why be miserable if you are not drinking? By cutting down you are not stopping drinking, but ingraining into your mind that alcohol is even more precious than you already thought it was, making you even more hooked than you were. The hook is mental not physical.

Chris Evans (British radio and TV personality) was talking about alcohol on his old morning radio show, (this is not unusual as he seems to be obsessed with the stuff). The reality is that he is so hooked that there was not ONE morning show that I have listened to where he didn't mention the drug at least once. He is well and truly hooked and even senses it, but he is in no position to admit it.

Chris Evans was talking about a new book that had just been released at the time 'how to drink without getting drunk' or something along those lines. He explained that the way to not get drunk at a dinner party while still drinking, was this (according to this book). When you first want a sip of your wine, don't! Just bring it up towards your mouth and instead of taking a drink, you should 'NOSE IT'. The next time you want a drink, you take a sip of water instead of the wine and only the third time should you actually take a drink. After that you repeat the whole process over again, and by doing this you can drink without getting drunk. OH WHAT FUN! This is cutting down on a supreme level, an intolerable level, a pathetic level. What scares me more than anything else is that the people who give this advice are taken seriously!

Let's get it clear that cutting down is not in any way a stepping stone to quitting. Like everything else when it comes to alcohol, it does the complete opposite to what we thought it did. We are dealing with a drug that cannot be controlled and that is why, in order to remain free for ever we should never fall for ...

29

"Oh, Just The One."

This is without doubt one of the most important chapters in the whole book. To ensure that you have lifelong success, you should clearly understand that THERE IS NO SUCH THING AS ONE DRINK!

What got us all hooked in the first place? It was just the thought of trying 'one' that got us started. This is where most people who stop drinking make a big mistake, they believe that there is no such thing as just 'one' drink for *them*. This makes them feel deprived, but the reality is that there is no such thing as 'just one' drink for *anybody!* The reason for this has nothing whatsoever to do with your genetic make-up, character, or personality, it is because alcohol is a drug and as such it plays with your mind. If you believe that you will obtain a benefit from *one* drink then you will also think that there is benefit in a million! There is no such thing as 'just one' fix of heroin for you either...why is that? Is it because of your personality? Because of your genetic make up? Or is it because of the nature of the drug? Again, you really don't need to be Sherlock Holmes to work it out.

Sometimes drinkers will say to me, *"What's wrong with you, you mean to say you can't have 'just one?"* I reply with honesty. *"Yes of course I can, but I do not want to".* I could always turn the table and say the same thing back to them. After all there is no such thing as

ONE drink for anyone, especially drinkers. I could easily say *"What's wrong with you, you mean to say you can't have 'just one?"* I would never do that as I know that there is nothing wrong with them – it is the drug that is the problem. This point must be very clear.

Drinking is a chain reaction that will last for the rest of your life, unless you break it. It is a disease which gets progressively worse and worse, unless you cure it. "Cured" means making absolutely certain that whatever happens you NEVER have 'just the one'! Make sure that you never recreate the disease ever again. It is a myth about the odd or 'special' drink that keeps people in what is known as 'recovery' when they have already stopped or gets them hooked again.

The reason why you will be hooked immediately if you have just one drink, is not because alcohol is so physically addictive. If it were, you would be hooked again by simply having a piece of chicken in white wine sauce! It is not because the physical withdrawal from one drink is so awful. It is because if you see a genuine pleasure in just one drink, then you will see a genuine pleasure in thousands of drinks.

About seven or eight months after gaining my freedom, I was in a bar on holiday. I had a glass of sparkling mineral water and my friend had a glass of wine. We were playing pool and, as she was taking her shot, I picked up what I thought was my water. It turned out to be her wine. It tasted disgusting! Just like that very first ever drink. So why didn't I get hooked again although I had taken a gulp of her wine? It is because there was not one part of me that actually *wanted* it, it was just a simple mistake. But at no time did I ever *want* it. At no point did I pick up the drink intentionally with the belief that I would gain pleasure from it. I didn't pick it up and think "oh, that would be nice, a glass of wine" I thought it was my water and couldn't actually believe just how revolting it tasted after all that time.

Nonetheless, even though it tasted awful, if I had thought for one second that I would get some kind of genuine pleasure from it before I had it, I would have been hooked! Taste has got nothing to do with it, your first drink was disgusting, did that stop you drinking? Of course it didn't, we are dealing with DRUG ADDICTION, so wake up and see it for what it is, not just for now, but for the rest of your life.

Whenever you think about alcohol, see it for what it actually is, and not the billions of pounds in advertising and brainwashing. It's time to regain control and advertise reality in your own mind.

There is no genuine pleasure in imbibing alcohol, so what would be the point in the 'one' drink anyway? If you did have ONE, what on earth do you think would ever prevent you from having the ONE more after that, and the ONE more after that one? NOTHING would stop you. Because it is not a habit or pleasure it is simple and straightforward drug addiction.

Alcohol does nothing for you, so the only time you would even contemplate having 'just the one' is if you thought you were missing out on a genuine pleasure. But if I have to repeat this point a million times and scream it from the roof tops I will – when you stop drinking you are giving up absolutely –

NOTHING!

Oh sorry apart from the headaches, the hangovers, the lethargy, the bad breath, the beer gut, the arguments, the violence, getting overemotional, regretting things that you have done that you cannot remember doing. Getting things out of all proportion, the snappy head, putting things off all the time, a vast bulk of your stress, the overdraft, the taxis, the guilt, the lies, the deceit, the brewer's droop, the mood swings, the constant breakdown of the immune system, the lack of resistance to all kinds of diseases, the destruction of brain-cells, the excess weight! Oh and yes I nearly forgot, what you will be 'giving up' most of all is –

THE DAILY MENTAL AND PHYSICAL SLAVERY OF BEING A DRUG ADDICT.

Giving up one of the worst diseases you will ever suffer from, giving up being controlled, being dictated to by a drug, giving up not being yourself on a regular basis! And last but by no means least, giving up kebabs, after all you would never eat them sober would you?

So now you can see that there is nothing to give up and you will feel no sense of sacrifice whatsoever. If you believe that now, why would you ever get uptight or miserable without alcohol and what power on earth could ever get you to convince yourself that you 'need' just that ONE more?

The answer is the same thing that got you hooked in the first place. In order to have life long success and to make certain that you are never fooled into having "one", you need to understand the clear difference between...

30
Curiosity vs. Craving

If you want to not just stop drinking, but make sure you remain free, please make sure you are wide awake when you read this chapter. Knowing the difference between curiosity and craving is perhaps the most important aspect of staying free.

Before we started drinking alcohol we didn't *need* it. The brainwashing seeped in slowly and we felt as though something was missing. Our friends were trying it, our parents did it, our role models were drinking it, so we thought that we were missing out on something that they were getting. We weren't sure what it was but we became **'curious'** to try some. This would NOT have been an overwhelming craving. If we had been told at this point that there would be no alcohol at the next jelly and ice-cream party, it wouldn't have bothered us because we did not drink and hadn't yet created a **craving** or fear that life would not be enjoyable without alcohol. The 'craving' only begins when you think that you are missing out on a genuine pleasure.

I wanted a drink before I even started drinking, that is why I had one. The reason for me wanting a drink was not because I used to be a drinker (because I had never had a drink in my life) and it had nothing to do with having alcohol circulating in my body, (because there wasn't any). My wanting was simply due to the massive brainwashing that I had been bombarded with since birth. It made me *curious* to try 'one'.

The brainwashing is still out there when you stop, but there will now be a big difference, you know its all rubbish! You are one of the few people who will see it for what it actually is. This will give you a sense of uniqueness, self-confidence, joy and euphoria on an ongoing basis. You will be better prepared after finishing this book than those few people who have never got hooked on alcohol. The trap is out there and anyone can fall into it at any time. Even people who have never drunk believe that alcohol relieves stress and makes people happy. They believe some of the brainwashing, but take the attitude *'what I've never had I won't miss and I don't want the bad side thank you'*. You should now realise that alcohol does nothing, not just for you, but anybody. The drug will never change, only your perception can change, which is why it is so important to understand what got you hooked in the first place so you can easily avoid it in the future. The aim of this book is not simply to help you stop drinking easily, but to show you just how easy it is to remain free for the rest of your life.

I was 'curious' to try the drug Ecstasy in the eighties. Everyone was doing it, or so it seemed. The people taking the drug were always trying to sell it. I don't mean sell it as in make a financial gain, but sell the 'effects' of the drug. Now I am relieved that I never fell for that trap. I never took the drug, but I did come close. This was 'curiosity' not 'craving' there is a big difference;

A craving is nothing more than the belief that some emotion will change internal representation of how you perceive something

In other words, if you always see alcohol as it actually is, and not as other drinkers or the alcohol industry wants you to see it, then you will never *crave* it ever again. You can't crave disease and slavery. As I have mentioned, I never took Ecstasy, but I had the choice to take a tablet whenever I wished. Just as you have the choice to take heroin if you wish. But, had I tried it, and the illusionary effects of the drug had confirmed the brainwashing then the 'curiosity' would have turned into 'craving'. I would have been hooked right then and there and my freedom of choice would have also vanished at the same time. There are many people who now feel as though they *cannot* go out without taking one, two, three or more Ecstasy tablets. Can you imagine being so dependent on a drug that you feel as though you cannot enjoy yourself as much without the drug? You really do not have to think that hard, as an alcohol addict you do precisely that.

To ensure your total freedom for life, you must understand that you may get 'curious' again. This curiosity is not there because you used to drink, it is not a *craving,* nor is it a genuine desire to drink, it is simply an 'ACTION SIGNAL'. It is telling you to take action, to *retune* yourself. It is a signal to remind yourself of the nature of brainwashing. It is a signal reminding you just how powerful this brainwashing can be. It is meant to serve you and to remind you just how wonderful it is to be free from the slavery of drug addiction! If there is one advantage at all to drinking it is that when you are free, you always have something to compare it with. You can very selfishly go on rejoicing for the rest of your life that you are free. After you are totally free and have been for a while, you sometimes forget all about drinking. So it is actually good to have these moments at times to remind you of your freedom and so you can once again retune and see alcohol addicts as they are. These moments of curiosity, if you get them at all, are no more than parts of the brainwashing creeping back in. It is a way to retune yourself and again jump for joy that you are free from that slavery. It is a way to flush the rubbish from your brain. Our bodies become polluted all the time due to outside sources, traffic, dust, dirt, etc.., and the body being the ultimate survival machine will do everything in its power to rid itself of those outside pollutants. This is to help you improve the quality and length of your life. Our minds are also being constantly polluted due to outside sources and it is *our* job to rid our minds of these pollutants. The alcohol industry is a drug industry. It has no morals and does not give a hoot about the quality of your life. Like all drug pushers they are out to make money. They will use any method possible to get people dependent on their drug. They know that if you hit their 'button' a few times, you will become dependent. They lose over a million customers a year around the world and that is just the ones who die. So they have to recruit as many new ones as possible. The first fix of any drug is free. That is why they will often sponsor student bashes. The people handing out 'free' bottles of beer are young people in the prime of their lives. They get people that look great to sell their drug. It is funny how they do not recruit someone who has just had their leg removed because of bad circulation due to what is apparently a 'happy pill'. They do not choose a middle aged man with puffy red cheeks, pricked and inflated nose, who is overweight and has lost family, house, and job because of alcohol. You can sell an illusion and image but not the real thing. You will soon find that just as your body automatically rids itself of outside pollutants, your mind will automatically filter any brainwashing that tries to creep back in.

When you stop drinking the facts about drinking will NEVER change, but their relevance to you changes completely because you have stopped. You are not worried about your health any more, because you feel a thousand times better. You are not worried about the money you were spending on the drug, and you are no longer worried about being a slave to something or being controlled by something. In other words you forget why you stopped in the first place, you forget how bad you felt, you forget the truth behind the drug. These are the times to remind yourself of the truth and to feel elated once again because you know the truth behind the confidence trick and to realise once again that the people who are drinking are the ones who are missing out.

Will this pose any problem? Is this simply a way to fight a genuine desire to drink? Will this happen all the time? Is this just like 'recovery'? NO NO NO, far from it, in reality these moments go as quickly as they come, if they come at all. This is not a genuine desire to drink at all. To be honest, I am only putting this in the book to make certain that you understand the trap fully, so should anything like this arise you don't question it, or worry about it. You will simply recognise it as an *action signal*, and once again jump for joy that you are free from that drug and don't *have* to do it anymore. This is a way of using your own mind as the most powerful tool on the planet to wipe out any brainwashing **immediately,** should it ever rear its ugly head again. This means that *you* will always be **in** control and not having to exercise control. There is a big difference, one is total freedom, the other is self-imposed slavery and manipulation on a massive scale!

There are people in really bad relationships, sometimes they have been physically and mentally abused for years, but *fear* keeps them locked in the relationship. One day they reach threshold and say *"I've had it"* and they finally pluck up the courage to break free. Once free they might feel a slight void one day, they might be bored one evening for example, they then make the big mistake of forgetting what it was really like and start remembering the good times. They then pick up the phone to their ex partner and WHAM! They are back exactly where they started. They can clearly see that they are stuck again but now find it even harder to get out, and are trapped once again.

With alcohol, you should remember there were never any good times, you were happy because of the company, the dancing, the party, the holiday, or the fact that it was your birthday, or Christmas but NOT because you were drinking. It was one big illusion designed to keep you trapped.

If you are bored one day, this does not mean you are low on alcohol! If you do get stressed about something after you stop, the cause of this problem is not alcohol deficiency. Life is not always a bed of roses whether you drink alcohol or not, but because you will be physically and mentally so much stronger, the highs will be much higher than before and the lows will be nowhere near as low as they used to be.

By this stage in the book you now should clearly realise that there is absolutely nothing to give up and that you are making no sacrifice at all by quitting alcohol. You now know that the craving was purely psychological and never physical. You also now realise that it is the poor drinker who will be deprived and missing out and not you. You know for certain that all traces of alcohol leave the body within 3–10 days. And if you have opened your mind you will see clearly that there is no such thing as an alcoholic and that everybody who drinks is hooked, like everybody else. Now that you know all of this when exactly is the best time to finally call.

31

Time Please Ladies And Gentlemen?

 So when exactly is the best time to call 'Time Please' to finally put an end to this addiction once and for all? When is the best time to free yourself of a slow and progressive disease? When is it right to stop?

NOW!

Alcohol addiction is a disease in itself which only gets worse and worse. When is the best time to cure yourself of any disease and gain total freedom in the process?

People's lives get slowly worse because of alcohol and they react by taking more. Other people then keep on at them to stop and tell them that they are out of control. This makes them feel even more insecure – so what do they turn to? When will it stop? The answer is 'never' if nobody points out what is really happening. It can and will just get worse and worse and worse.

You have already made up your mind that you not going to spend the rest of your life as an alcohol addict, so at some point you are going to stop whether you find it easy or difficult. It is only FEAR that keeps people hooked; don't allow this FALSE fear to keep you hooked for the rest of your life. That is exactly what these fears are anyway –

FALSE! The nature of the drug is to fool you. Your problem was that you genuinely thought that alcohol gave you some kind of genuine pleasure or crutch and your fear was not being able to enjoy your life or cope without alcohol. The reason you thought this is because you had evidence to back up your fears. Even going 'on the wagon', which gave you the evidence to back up your fear that you would be miserable without a drink. But the fears you have are all false, they only *appear* real because of past attempts to stop or cut down. These fears will not recreate themselves because they were only a result of failing to understand the nature of the disease and suffering from the CAN'T syndrome (Constant And Never-ending Torture). In other words the fears created by alcohol mean,

False Evidence which *Appears* Real

In other words the FEAR people have of stopping drinking *Appears Real* because of the illusionary effects of alcohol, which are **False**. The illusions are giving you *False Evidence* that *Appears Real* to you.

Going back to the wonderful film *The Wizard Of Oz*, if you recall the big evil wizard never actually existed. In reality, the scary booming voice which created such incredible fears for Dorothy, the tin man, the straw man and the lion, was in reality completely false. But because they couldn't see the reality, the *false evidence* that the voice must belong to something that could destroy them *appeared real* – and so created a false FEAR which prevented them from moving forward and finding their true selves. Yet all it took for all of their fears to be removed was to see the truth. They pushed a button which opened some curtains to reveal a small old man speaking into a microphone and moving some machinery in order to create the illusion. Once they saw this there is just no way on earth that the voice could ever create feelings of fear within any of them again, and the minute they knew there was nothing to fear they moved forward.

Just like the Wizard Of Oz, there has *never* been anything to fear. The truth is there is nothing to fear at all by stopping drinking and *everything* to fear by continuing. So what is the best time to get free from any disease? When is the best time to free yourself from mental and physical slavery? What is really the best time to quit alcohol?

The answer is obvious –

A.S.A.P!

It's similar to taking your driving test, you feel nervous for sure, but once you have passed you feel euphoric at that point. At what point does the drinker know they are free? Answer: the very second they see it for what it is, finish their final drink and say *"That's it. It's over, it's finished, I am NOW FREE!"* If they do this they are not in remission or recovery – they are FREE.

The beauty about becoming free is that you don't need to wait for anything to happen, because nothing is going to happen. It is the waiting for something to happen which creates doubts and fears. Once you have *decided* never to drink again then that's it, it is over at that point. You can jump for joy at that moment!

The key to life long success is to truly decide. Not to *hope, would, should* or *could* but KNOW FOR CERTAIN that you will never drink again. If you *hope* you are going on holiday it doesn't mean you are going anywhere, but if you *know for certain,* then you will go for certain. Once you make a true decision you cut off any other possibility. That is what decision means in its Latin form; *'to cut off from'* to remove any other possibility, so whatever happens in your future life, drinking alcohol is just not an option. It is something that you have no interest in doing. You have moved on and are free.

Let's make something very clear, the decision never to drink again is without doubt one of the most important decisions you will ever make in your entire life. The reality is that both the length and the daily quality of your future life depends on this decision. There is nothing that is more important than the length and quality of your future life. Some people say to me *"Oh yeah, but you can get run over by a bus next week",* of course you can, but would you take heroin because you could get run over by a bus next week? Would you deliberately keep jumping in front of buses? Of course you wouldn't! There is a bus coming along for all of us, it's the daily *quality* of our lives that counts. It is how we feel TODAY! It's making sure that we are in control of our lives before the bus comes along that ultimately counts. Making sure that we have our true courage, our true confidence and our true freedom on a daily basis. To not be dependent, so that we can enjoy the juice of life again.

Alcohol, and the brainwashing involved, created so much fear in my mind, that I simply thought what would be the point in living longer if I could not drink. Once I realised that I was in a sense my own jailor, then my fears that had seemed so real and so strong, were shown to be false. Once it began to dawn on me that those fears and insecurities were CAUSED by alcohol itself and were not real, then the decision never to drink again became the EASIEST decision I have ever made in my life. I knew I was free even before I had my final drink. And once I had finished my last ever alcohol drink, I jumped for joy. I had been questioning my drinking for weeks beforehand, asking myself if it was the drink that made the evening or the company. I watched 'other drinkers' permanently trying to justify why they needed that particular drink, even though it was only Monday night! I knew that it didn't do anything, I could clearly see this even before I had stopped. When I woke up on the morning after my final drink, I initially felt terrible, but as I slowly woke up, the first thing I thought was *"I'm free"*. It was one of the best feelings I have ever had, and I have never lost it. I thought that it would be difficult for a few weeks, but far from it, I had made the CONCRETE DECISION *never* to be dependent on alcohol ever again. Once you make a true decision then you're free.

I cannot stress enough just how easy it is to stop drinking and, when simplified, it really only comes down to few things;

1. Decide never to drink alcohol again.
2. Don't sit around moping about it – jump for joy that you're free!
3. Get some live nutrients flowing through your system in the first week.

That's it. It really *can* be that simple. It is only the indecision and moping about not drinking that makes it difficult. The withdrawal from alcohol is no more and no less than a hangover, and we have all dealt with many of those in the past. If you start with a feeling of excitement and freedom you won't even be aware of it. You will be too relieved and happy to be bothered about any slight physical withdrawal from alcohol. Why didn't I suffer withdrawal pangs when I stopped drinking? Because they do not exist. It is the doubt and uncertainty that causes the pangs which some people describe as *withdrawal*. It is all in the mind, which is why it is so important to start with a happy frame of mind, then the adjustment period will be easy and enjoyable. I have said that it is important to finish reading *all* of this book. That way you will find freedom not only easy to achieve and enjoyable, but most importantly, you will find it permanent. If you have understood the trap at this stage I cannot blame you for being like Mr Itch of Itching Town to break free. But wait. It is *essential* that you fully understand ......

32

The Adjustment Period

Some people call this the withdrawal period, but withdrawal from what? Your body has never *craved* alcohol and it never will. Your body has only ever wanted to get rid of the poison. The word *withdrawal* itself can give the impression of trauma and some degree of pain. Physical withdrawal simply means *repair.* It needs to be fully understood as such. That is what a hangover is, the body doing it's best to get rid of the poison for you. It is simply a way of keeping you alive. In truth even the physical *withdrawal* (repair) is a good thing too. It is purging the poison from your body and with it goes any remaining brainwashing from your mind. Even if you are a heavy drinker and your body is shaking slightly after you stop, it is simply part of the process of getting rid of the poison. It is just part of the body's need to repair, which happens incredibly quickly. If you see it for what it is you will even enjoy the process. We now know that any physical aggravation after the first morning is very subtle and will be gone within ten days, (for most people it is only three days). The mental *adjustment* period lasts slightly longer, but in reality can be the most enjoyable part of stopping drinking. Let me explain. If you have a car for a few years and the indicators are on one side of the steering column and windscreen wipers on the other side, isn't it true that when you buy another car they always seem to be on the opposite side? It is the law of the sod as they say. What happens at the beginning when you want to indicate? The windscreen wipers come on. Did you want to turn them on? NO. You wanted to indicate. So why didn't you? It is because your brain has been conditioned for so long that it just does it automatically. The brain just needs a little while to *adjust*. The adjustment period takes from one to three weeks. After this time things become even clearer. This happens when you are mentally and physically completely outside the cage.

Let me ask you a question; If you made the mistake of putting on your wipers instead of indicating would you stare at the wipers and say to yourself *"Oh no I can't get the hang of this new car, I will never adjust. I will have to have my old car back because if I stay in this one, people behind me will never know which way I'm turning and I'll be in a muddle every time I try an indicate"*? Of course you wouldn't. Would you even worry about it? Would you even give it a second thought? The reality is that you laugh when you put the wipers on instead of the indicators and you are doing it every ten minutes the first day. But does it bother you? The answer is no, of course not. Why not? It simply comes down to the fact that you are not just **hoping** that your brain and body will adjust, **YOU KNOW FOR CERTAIN** that they will definitely adjust. The **knowing** for certain has destroyed any doubt, and that is why it doesn't bother you in the slightest. That is how powerful a sense of certainty really is. That is why after you finish your final drink, you will *know* it is over rather than *hope* that it might be over. Whether you find it easy or not depends on how you think.

You have been conditioned to take it at certain times depending on just how far into the trap you are. It can range from first thing in the morning to weekends, lunchtime, with dinner, as you come in from work, etc. The point that I am making is that after you stop you will still be coming home from work, still socialising, still eating (of course) and still waking up! That is why you need to understand that your brain and body will easily *adjust,* providing you let it and providing you don't worry about it. Any triggers that may occur over the first few weeks work in exactly the same way as the wiper-indicator situation. These are times to feel relieved and excited. You may even get thoughts every now and then of *"I want a drink"*. It is nothing to worry about and it is 'only a thought'. We do not act on all of our thoughts, if we did, most of us would be in jail! It's understanding these thoughts that makes the whole business of stopping easy, enjoyable and permanent. If you ever get one of these thoughts it doesn't mean that something is going wrong, it is just the windscreen wipers in your mind flicking back to the old pattern for a split second. If you say to yourself at these times "I *mustn't* have one", "I *can't* have one" or *"when* will I be free" then you will be defeating the whole object of the exercise and you will become a whinging ex-drinker. Just indicate, adjust, rejoice and move on. This is one of the most enjoyable parts of stopping drinking. These are the times when you can remind yourself *"I don't need to do that anymore, I'm free"*. You can and will enjoy these moments, if or when triggers occur over the first couple of weeks. This is *adjustment* and not *willpower.* Do not confuse them.

Willpower is when you are constantly fighting a genuine desire to do something that you still want to do. If you think for one second that you are using willpower, you will start to create doubt and where there is doubt there is uncertainty and where there is uncertainty there is always an element of willpower. If you experience the trigger, *"I want a drink"* and you believe in your gut and mind that the alcohol itself will genuinely benefit you in any way, then you have missed the point, you will switch on to willpower and be back in the pit in no time at all. But if you experience the trigger *"I want a drink"* and you know that there are genuinely no benefits, you will understand that it is simply a trigger and it will be dismissed as quickly as you would turn your windscreen wipers off and indicators on. *Will I have to do this all of my life?* Did you have to constantly switch from wiper to indicator all of your life? Of course not. How long did it take to fully adjust to the new car? The first day you may have been putting the wipers on every ten minutes, but the next day it was HALVED and the day after that halved again and within one to two weeks you weren't doing it anymore. You were *fully adjusted.* The reality is that it probably seemed to be a lot less because it was so easy to do and you were not waiting for anything to happen. At the same time you would be so pleased with your brand new vehicle that the last thing you would be concerned about is putting your wipers on! And every time the wipers did come on you did not use *willpower* to indicate, you **want** to indicate. Willpower is when you go against what you want.

Every now and then you will still put the wipers on first, but how often? You will probably do it maybe once or twice a year, but you indicate so quickly, in other words it is so automatic that you don't even notice what you have done. It is the same with alcohol, you will retune yourself easily so many times during the first couple of weeks and love the process that it will simply become automatic.

So see this adjustment for what it is. You are starving a disease to death. You are now in charge of something that was controlling you. That is exactly how I saw it. I had been feeding a disease that was controlling many aspects of my life because I was fooled into thinking that it was my friend! I thought it was helping me to enjoy life more and cope with stresses. When I realised that it was always doing the complete opposite and that it created feelings of insecurity, I rejoiced in staving it to death. I did not use willpower, because I didn't *want* to feed it. I wanted it out of my life for good. If you see it like this you will love the adjustment period. What is there to feel miserable about? NOTHING! The sad reality about any drug addiction is that it is the addict who *has* to use willpower, discipline and control on an ongoing basis which can last for the rest of his life. Once the nature of this drug is fully understood, you do not need willpower, discipline or control. You will finally be free from having to exercise control.

In one of my consultations a gentleman at the beginning of the session said *"it would be so nice if you could just put me a couple of weeks into the future, so that the worst is over"*. At the end of the session he wanted the adjustment period just so that he could witness the disease starving to death. He *wanted* to starve it, he wanted some revenge. He realised at the end of the session that the worst was already over – he didn't *need* or *want* drink anymore! As he put it *"What would be the point?"* Another common misconception is that if you are truly free from alcohol then you should no longer even think about drinking. This can also create doubt if not fully understood. So let us now cover the very important point that you will definitely ....

33

Think Drink

 You will be thinking about drinking quite a lot over the first few weeks, but it is *what* you think that makes the difference. I remember on one of my attempts to go 'on the wagon' for a week, all I thought about was drinking. I was waiting for the day I could drink again. I felt miserable and deprived, I was having a mental tantrum all week. The thinking about drinking was not the problem it was *how* I was thinking. When I did finally stop completely I also thought about drinking, but I did so in a new light. I did not have a mental tantrum and was not staying in and whinging away. Every time I thought about drinking I was elated to be free and I couldn't wait to go out and prove, not only to myself, but to the world that you do not need alcohol.

A very common mistake that people make when *attempting* to stop drinking, is trying not to think of alcohol or worrying about it if they are. Have you ever tried to do that? Have you ever tried <u>not</u> to think of something? It is IMPOSSIBLE to try not to think of something. The fact that you are trying not to think of it means that you are thinking about it. Let me try an experiment with you. Try not to think of Michael Jackson. What are you thinking about right now? The point I'm making is that you will of course think about alcohol after you stop, but it really is only <u>what</u> you think that makes the difference.

Do you believe that Nelson Mandela never thought about the prison he was in for twenty-seven years after he was released? Of course he did. In fact he probably thought about it a lot more during the first few weeks of his release than he does now. But does it mean that if he is thinking about prison he must secretly be missing it? Of course not. Does he ever think; *"Oh I'd love to go back there, just for my birthday, but what a shame I can't"*. You must be joking! Especially if he new that if he did he would have to spend the rest of his life in there! Every time he thinks about prison life he must think *'Isn't it wonderful I'm free'*. He must feel sheer relief in his mind to know that he is no longer being controlled, but in control.

That is exactly how I think about alcohol now. I think about alcohol a lot, as you can imagine, it's the nature of what I do and it is my mission to *cure* the world of this disease, but I NEVER think I'm missing out, so therefore I *never* have a problem. I am just so grateful that I saw the problem when I did and that I am now in control every day. In order for me to think that I was missing out I would have to lie to myself. I would have to convince myself that I was being deprived. That would now be impossible because I understand the confidence tricks and once you know how any trick works you will never be able to believe the illusion again. Nobody could ever convince me otherwise. Once you know the truth, you can not be fooled.

As I illustrated in the chapter on advertising, it would be almost impossible to forget alcohol. It is the most advertised and accepted drug in the world and at the moment at least 90% of the UK are hooked. It is the thinking about drinking that is the "key to success", the seeing it for what it actually is. It all acts as a wonderful reminder of just how relieved you will feel to be free.

If you are thinking about alcohol over the first few weeks, so what! You were thinking about alcohol anyway a lot more than you realised. I will repeat this a thousand times, alcohol addicts whether conscious or not, are having to exercise willpower, discipline and some degree of control most of the time. It is only certain restrictions that prevent them from increasing their intake, making their descent to the bottom slightly slower. The rate of descent will vary from one alcohol addict to the next, due to the restrictions they have and their physical capability of coping with the poisonous drug. However, they are all going in one direction....DOWN!

I think about heroin sometimes. It is frequently mentioned in the news and when it is, I think about it. It really doesn't matter that I think about it because I simply think what a shame for those poor addicts. That is exactly how I think about alcohol now, I simply think what a shame for those poor addicts. I feel even sadder when I realise that most are unaware of the fact that they are sinking. When I think about alcohol now I just think, how come I didn't see it earlier? It is all so obvious to me now. Alcohol is a drug like any other and once you see it for what it is, and are relieved to be free, it would not matter if you thought about alcohol twenty four hours a day, you would still be happy.

Another big mistake that people make when stopping drinking is that they try to avoid …

34

Tempting Situations

What tempting situations are we talking about? There aren't any, they don't exist! If you were pulled from quicksand would you need to avoid certain situations in case you were tempted to jump back in? If you don't want or need to drink and are relieved to be free, why would you need to avoid certain situations? The beauty with understanding the nature of the 'alcohol trap' is that you do not have to avoid any situations. One of the key instructions in this book is to make certain that you don't. Every single moment that we have is to be savoured and not avoided. When I was 'on the wagon' for those three months I tried to avoid certain situations where I thought I would be tempted to drink. I avoided going out and socialising where possible. When I did go out during those three months, I felt even more miserable than before. I still thought at that time that *I* was missing out! I felt a lot more tempted to drink at these times than at any other time. This is why people assume that it's logical to avoid situations where you might be tempted. But if you are tempted then you are tempted. If you believe that you are making a genuine sacrifice then the instruction to avoid situations where you might be tempted is ridiculous anyway. For how long exactly should you avoid social gatherings and going out for meals? Well according to organisations like AA – FOREVER! That's a pretty daunting prospect isn't it? It really would confirm your belief that life is dull, boring and miserable without a drink. This will in turn create even greater feelings of deprivation causing you to feel more than *tempted* to have a drink. This is what they call 'recovery'! That is exactly what happened to me during those three months. The instruction is even more stupid when you realise that some people are tempted to drink when they first wake up. So does this mean that they should never wake up ever again in case they get tempted? (That would certainly solve their drink problem wouldn't it?)

I cannot stress this point enough. There is no need whatsoever to avoid any situation that comes along, in fact it is important that you don't, otherwise you will start to think that life is not as enjoyable without a drink. People often ask me *"Should I avoid pubs?"* – Why? That would be the same as vegetarians avoiding restaurants in case they are tempted to have a T.Bone steak! Vegetarians are not tempted to eat meat even if everybody else is, regardless of the situation they are in. They cannot be tempted because they do not want meat. There is no need at all to avoid any situations, including pubs. You may, however, find yourself no longer experiencing the desire to visit pubs all the time. When you are sober you start to notice things like flock wallpaper and floral carpets, cigarette burns, the stench of alcohol, the mood changes and the overall dingy atmosphere of many pubs. The toilets are often awful. Men miss the toilet at the best of times, but when they are drunk – no chance!

I believe that many pubs should be renamed to give them a more realistic feel. Instead of 'Ye Old Inn', 'The White Horse', 'The Crown and Anchor', how about 'Ye Old Vomit-INN' or 'The Clown and Wanker' or 'The Violent Tavern'.

Am I implying that all pubs are like this? NO! But you do need to realise that the main point of pubs is for people to get their fix of a drug. I still go to some pubs, wine bars and clubs. If I am having a great time, excellent. If not, I know that a drink will not make the evening better, I realise that it is just a lousy evening or I am just not in the mood. I am *never* genuinely tempted to drink, in fact the complete opposite. I go for the company, to socialise and to have fun. This can sometimes be difficult to do in your regular run down, smoke infested, dirty, dingy local. Once you are sober and physically and mentally free you will start to see just how much more to life there really is than going to the same dingy building every night!

There is no need whatsoever to avoid these places for fear of being tempted. Do not change your life in any way (unless you were going to change it anyway). If you are used to having a drink with a meal, still have the meal! If you're used to joining your friends at lunch time in a wine bar, then still join your friends. I have already explained how alcohol does nothing for you or anybody else, so you will be missing out on absolutely *nothing*. But if you were to avoid that particular situation deliberately, then you would be missing out – on living! Remember you are stopping drinking – not living. Once the poison has fully left your mind and body it will not matter if it's New Year, your birthday, or a holiday – you simply will not miss drinking. You will be able to celebrate just like you used to at these times; dancing, good company, fireworks, good friends, laughing and having a blast! The difference will be that you will remember the entire evening, you will be 'under the influence' of *you* the entire evening, you will wake up feeling refreshed and alive, and you will be able to drive home – always!

This is another huge part of the alcohol problem, not only in this country but throughout the world. The brainwashing is so severe that the word 'celebrate' is linked to a drug, that drug being alcohol. This is because from the moment we are born we have been subjected to thousands of images of people celebrating *all* events with alcohol. Whether it's a birthday or a lottery win, drinkers will look for any excuse to celebrate, which means 'having a drink'. Sport is always a good one. If your team wins, have a drink. If your team loses have a drink! One is to celebrate, one to drown your sorrows. If you do win the lottery, the first thing they do is bring you a bottle of champagne (which is nothing more than a hyped up fizzy gone off fruit anyway). We have been so conditioned to link alcohol with celebration, that Paul Merson, (the English footballer I spoke of earlier), was even presented with a bottle of champagne for winning 'Man of the Match' *after* he told the world that he was an *alcoholic!* Were they on a wind up? A woman once came to see me for a stop smoking session. At the end of the session she was the only one in the small group who didn't look very excited (which is unusual). I asked her if she looked forward to being a non-smoker, and her answer came as something of a shock. *"I was feeling really good, until you told me to go out and celebrate"*. I said *"what on earth is wrong with going out to celebrate and why wouldn't you want to do so?"* She replied *"I am a 'recovering' alcoholic and you have just told me to have a drink, that is very inconsiderate of you and I now realise that I cannot truly celebrate"*. I must admit that I thought I was hearing things. I had never once told her to go out and have a drink to celebrate, I had simply said 'celebrate'. I had almost forgotten that nearly everyone links that word with alcohol. Eric Clapton (musician) holds a New Years Eve party where all the guests are ex-addicts of some kind. He feels as though he cannot 'celebrate' with *normal* people and holds an annual party for people in a similar position to himself. But why can't he celebrate New Year with people who *need* to drink alcohol? What is stopping him? Only one thing – his belief. While he believes that he is *abnormal* for not drinking and believes that people who are drinking are *normal*, then he will always feel vulnerable. He will feel as though it's something in him and not the nature of the drug. Celebration = alcohol for the vast majority of people in this country. The two just go together. I used to believe this too, but not anymore. I am now in the same position as I was before I got sucked into this confidence trick. I celebrate by having nice people around me, good music, laughter, just having a good time and feeling good about the day or situation. It is sad to think that the woman at my clinic believes that she is still *recovering* from alcohol and yet she hasn't had a drink in three years. It is even sadder to think that she believes that the only thing she can ever celebrate is the fact that she has stayed sober for that day! But in her mind she cannot even celebrate that, because she believes that celebration means having a drink. She is not alone, so does nearly everyone in this country.

Remember you have gone through your drinking life feeling 'tempted', it was only 'restrictions' that prevented you from always giving in to that temptation. The beauty of seeing it for what it is, is to realise that you are no longer tempted and that you do not have to avoid situations because of alcohol. As already illustrated, alcohol addicts have to avoid certain situations all the time in case they do get tempted. They sometimes choose not go out if they have a big day ahead because they know they will *have* to drink if they do. The reason for avoiding the situation was for one reason alone, 'restrictions'. These may have been health, money, family, work, or whatever. This is without doubt the best part of the method, to make sure that you don't avoid any situation. It is one of my key instructions. I now go out more now than I ever did when I was hooked. There is no need to restrict myself anymore, there is no need for me to avoid any situation. I can go out seven nights a week if I wish and not have to worry about getting up and feeling like I've just been run over by a truck. I can afford to do so now. It is so cheap to go out when you don't need a drug to enjoy yourself or feel at one with yourself. The biggest difference when I go out now, is that I feel alive! I am me, I am my genuine character all of the time. Each day after you stop, your genuine courage and confidence returns and it happens quickly. It is like a muscle that builds gradually every single day, but it will only build if you use it, your true courage and confidence will not return if you sit indoors deliberately not going out in case you might be tempted!

You will start to notice your windscreen wipers coming on every now and then (to refer to the analogy I used earlier) but will also understand that by building a mental muscle, you are reversing the massive alcohol advertising and brainwashing which has made you, me and millions like us victims of a very clever confidence trick.

Remember, the pain of stopping drinking is a myth, it is all in the mind. It is easy to stop drinking. It was only the feeling of deprivation (a mental tantrum) that created the myth of 'recovery'. It was the feeling of 'missing out', which caused you to try and avoid situations when trying to stop or cut down on your drinking in the past. Not only do you no longer need to avoid situations, but for the first time, **you** can enjoy more of them, more of the time, with an added sense of freedom and joy in the knowledge that you are no longer a slave to a drug, but that you are truly free to actually live your life as you now choose.

So enjoy going out for a "non-drink", enjoy not *needing* a drink. It is a wonderful feeling, one that never goes away. Enjoy being IN control, rejoice in your freedom. You will not be free if you are avoiding situations, so don't avoid them, be totally free.

Another question that people often ask me is *"what do I drink instead of alcohol. What should I replace it with?"* The question seems logical, but another very important part of this method is to realise that you do not need and should not search for any kind of ....

35

Replacements

 One of the key instructions essential to success is that you:–

DO NOT SEARCH FOR A REPLACEMENT FOR ALCOHOL

We must get it clear in our minds that we do not need to constantly drink something when we are socialising. Some people say *"there are only so many orange juices you can drink"*. It's funny that they don't say the same thing with alcoholic drinks, isn't it?

The addiction to the drug known as alcohol is a disease, the disease ends the second you *stop* taking it. If you had a different progressive disease that was only going to get worse and worse, and you found a cure for it, would you be searching for a replacement for that disease after you were cured? Or would you simply breathe a sigh of relief that you didn't have the progressive disease any more? I know what I would do, which is exactly what I do quite often, breathe a sigh of relief that I do not have to suffer mentally or physically any more.

Why would anybody want a replacement for a disease? It doesn't make sense. People only want a replacement if they think they are missing out on a genuine pleasure, it's only because they still feel deprived. When people are driving, for example, they are in a sense forced not to drink alcohol, so they drink non-alcoholic beers and wines. The only reason for doing this is because they feel as though they have made a sacrifice. During the three months that I 'gave up' 'on the wagon', I tried loads of these non-alcoholic beers and wines, but I couldn't get to like them. This was simply because they had NO ALCOHOL IN THEM!

If you were to switch to non-alcoholic beer or wine, especially during the 'adjustment period' there is a danger that you would subconsciously be impressing on your mind that you had made a genuine sacrifice. This *could* act like a dripping tap and make you believe that you were missing out on something genuine. If you were to drink these non alcoholic drinks it would be exactly the same as a heroin addict, quitting heroin, but continuing to inject themselves with a substance that costs the same amount as heroin, looks like heroin, feels like heroin, but has NO HEROIN in it! Do you think that this would help them to get free, or drive them insane? Obviously, it would drive the addict insane, because the only reason for seeking a replacement in the first place was the feeling of missing out.

As for the statement, *"there are only so many orange juices you can drink"* there are millions of drinks that do not contain alcohol which taste wonderful. I drink plenty of them when I'm out and when I'm staying in. We need to drink as it is part of our survival mechanism, but we should only drink if we are thirsty. The reason that I could drink so much alcohol was because it was dehydrating me, so that I felt thirsty all the time. When you stop dehydrating your body, you will realise that you just don't need to drink on an ongoing basis. You will realise that a couple of drinks can last you all night.

I'm not saying that there aren't going to be times when water just isn't going to cut it, but there are many, many non-alcoholic drinks on the market (AME, Purdeys, etc) that actually taste pretty good. I'm also not saying that all of you will hate the taste of non-alcoholic wines and beers, I'm just saying that most of them are full of rubbish and there is a danger that you could easily send subconscious messages to your brain that you're missing out, which is the last thing you want.

There are many 'experts' who will tell you that if you stop drinking you need to replace it with something else. Like what? Meetings every week perhaps! You will find that after a while you do have new interests. Not as a result of 'replacing' but as a result of expanding your life and broadening your horizons. When you don't need to drink you will want to do a lot more with your life. This is not replacement, it's living.

If you think that you would like to drink these non-alcoholic beers and wines because drinking orange juice doesn't look 'very adult', then GROW UP! It was precisely that kind of thinking that got us trapped in the first place. People think that it doesn't look cool to drink a 'soft' drink. But it isn't very cool to get stupid, aggressive, argumentative, obnoxious, violent, uptight, hostile, physically sick, fall over, slur your words, collapse, or blow your mind either! Why isn't it cool to drink 'soft' drinks? Why is it seen as a sissy thing to do? Why is it seen as not very grown up? It is simply because of the brainwashing and conditioning, that's all. Even the word 'soft' implies that it is a weedy thing to do. *"Look everybody I'm on the 'HARD' stuff tonight, you have to drive so you are left having to drink the 'soft' stuff."* You see, it's all in the "over advertised" mind. *"But a pint of orange juice, is just the same price as a pint of beer, so what's the point in switching to soft drinks, it will cost just as much"*. What's the point? The point is to be free from drug addiction. And it won't cost anywhere near the same amount as being an alcohol addict anyway. As I have already said, alcohol dehydrates the body making you drink more and besides, money is not a factor in why people drink alcohol anyway, it's to get the effect of the drug. Having all the money in the world means nothing if you are a slave to a drug.

It is now very clear to me and will soon become just as clear to you, if it hasn't already happened, that you were substituting when you **were** drinking. You were replacing **TRUE** courage, **TRUE** confidence, **TRUE** relaxation, and the **TRUE** you with a **FALSE** substitute. One of the joys of stopping is to not have to substitute or replace anymore.

So now you realise that there is no genuine pleasure in alcohol. You realise that it causes insecurities and stress. Alcohol destroys your courage, undermines your confidence and is incapable of giving any genuine relaxation. You now also realise that you are suffering from a progressive disease which will only get worse and worse. You are in the trap and whether you knew it or not before picking up this book, it is now time to gain ultimate freedom from this slavery. It will be ultimate freedom from a disease that was undermining every area of your life, whether you were conscious of it or not. It is a confidence trick on a massive scale, the biggest one ever to plague humankind. Now that you can see it for what it is, it is time to get very excited, and time to realise that you do not *have* to continue drinking. It is now time to decide when you are going to have .....

36

The Final Drink

It all sounds very final doesn't it? THE FINAL DRINK gives an impression of sacrifice, (or it would do to over 90% of our population), but it won't to you. Any fear that you may have at this moment is also mixed with adrenalin and excitement. As I have already explained, there is nothing to fear at all, it was all false. The fear is the biggest part of the confidence trick, alcohol is designed to make people feel insecure without it in certain situations – it's what keeps people hooked.

There is nothing 'final' about the final drink, it simply spells a new beginning. You are achieving not only what you want to achieve, but in reality what every alcohol addict would love to achieve. To be able to enjoy and cope with life without having to drink. To be physically and mentally free from drug addiction forever. To no longer feel dependent.

We have been taught that being truly free from alcohol is impossible to achieve. We have been conditioned to believe in this mythical disease known as 'alcoholism' for which there is no known cure. We have been taught that if you do stop drinking you will only be able to expect a *satisfactory* way of life. This is simply because to alcohol addicts stopping drinking is like losing a close friend or relative. This would seem true if you thought that alcohol was always there when you needed it, always helping you through the stresses and strains of life. All this recovery nonsense is nothing more than a broken heart and people say there is no cure for a broken heart. When a close friend or relative dies we have to go through a mourning process, there is no physical pain but it is a real trauma and it can take years to get over. Even then there is a void which can last for the rest of our lives. This is what alcohol addicts put themselves through when they stop. This is why they believe that there is no cure, and why they would fear the thought of a *final* drink. They feel as though they are parting with a friend, and as far as they are concerned it really does spell the end. They will still feel a void for years after they have stopped. In some ways it is even worse for the poor alcohol addict than for the person who has lost a close friend. At least when a close friend dies, you can start the mourning process and your brain will accept after time that they are gone. The poor alcohol addict thinks that their old companion is still out there, but they cannot be friends anymore because THEY abused it! Everybody else can get the *benefits* of this friend, but they can't. That is what we are taught, that if you abuse alcohol you pay the price. ABUSE ALCOHOL? It was alcohol that inflicted the abuse. It was never the other way around.

Alcohol addicts who 'give up' will *start* with a feeling of doom and gloom, and that feeling of doom and gloom may stay with them forever. They are not losing a friend, however, but getting rid of a disease which would have affected the quality of life forever. In stopping drinking you are breaking free and achieving something that all drinkers would love to achieve. Have fun, rejoice in your freedom and enjoy letting the disease starve to death!

I have just finished reading a book called '*The Effective Way to Stop Drinking*' written by a man called Beauchamp Colclough. This book is a diatribe of doom and gloom. I am not directly criticising Beauchamp, in fact I feel sorry for him. He honestly believes that he is a *recovering alcoholic*, and because he believes it, he is! He states in his book and I quote;

"*Alcoholism is a fatal disease if it's not arrested. I use the word 'arrested' because there is no cure. A lot of people seem to think that, if you don't drink alcohol for a period of time, they will be able to continue drinking again. That is not the case. When a person with a drinking problem puts down the drink, the consequences surrounding the drinking problem cease; if that person picks up a drink again. Then he or she has got the problem back. It doesn't go away"*

What does he mean it doesn't go away? Of course the disease goes away. The chemical addiction to any drug is a disease that gets worse and worse. If you stop putting the CAUSE of the disease into your body then you are CURED! It is essential to know that you have got a disease in order to cure it, but isn't it just as important to know when you are cured? In reality, Beauchamp is not fully cured, he has no alcohol in his body, but still believes that he is making a genuine sacrifice. He is still fighting a desire to do something, which he doesn't want to do ever again!

To people like Beauchamp, Frank Skinner or the George Bests of this world, the final drink spells the end of a friend and the beginning of a battle that has to be fought every day for the rest of their lives. Is it any wonder that they feel so fearful about stopping? Is it any surprise that they feel so low when they stop? When I stopped six years ago I knew it was going to be different before I had even consumed my last drink. I could see it for what it was, the ending of a disease and the beginning of my freedom. I looked forward to having my last drink, not for the drink, but for knowledge that I was 100% certain that it was my last. What a wonderful feeling it was, a feeling that has never gone away.

So when should you have your final drink? What is the best time? Should you have it alone, with friends, indoors, outdoors? The choice is now yours. You have your final drink wherever you choose to have it. But make sure you have it. If you have already had your final drink and as far as you are concerned it's already over, then congratulations, you are now free. However, please finish this book as everything in it is here for a reason. If you haven't yet had your final drink then choose a time that suits you, but don't put it off. If you have understood what is in this book and you can see it clearly then you shouldn't want to put it off for a moment longer than necessary. If you are slightly apprehensive, then this is normal, it is only the last remainder of the false fear that was keeping you trapped. This will soon be dispelled in no time at all (as explained in the period of adjustment chapter).

Whatever your views were on alcohol before reading this book, now is the time to dump them for good. Remember:

THE PAST DOES NOT EQUAL THE FUTURE

It is what you do TODAY that counts. So many people bring unwanted failures with them through life, it weighs them down and fear that they won't succeed today because of what happened yesterday. RUBBISH! You will succeed, and it's easy. I have made a list of all the instructions, follow them and freedom is yours for the taking. It doesn't matter how long you have been drinking, what your intake has been or how many times you have *tried* in the past, *anybody* can find it easy and enjoyable to stop drinking. All you have to do is:

UNDERSTAND THE TRAP AND FOLLOW THE GUIDELINES.

You must get it clear that knowledge is nothing without the final ingredient to ultimate success, **ACTION!** So many people in life know what to do and how they can do it, but fail to do it. It's not what you know but what you do with what you know that counts. It is no good knowing what to do, without doing what you know. Why wouldn't you want to do it? There is no down side to this decision only an upside. What are the alternatives? Did you believe when you had your very first drink all those years ago that you would have to spend an indefinite number of years drinking? Did you ever believe that you would become dependent on it? Did you even consider that one day just the thought of stopping would put fear into you, when you had your first drink? Has it got better or worse? Unless you do stop this disease what will stop you from spending the rest of your life drinking?

I have already given you the instructions you need at stages throughout this book, but to simplify them here are ......

37

The Guidelines

1. DECISION

Make your decision that after the final drink you will never drink alcohol again. I have explained just how powerful a true decision really is. It cuts off all other possibilities, it gives an air of certainty that literally destroys any doubts. You must realise that you can easily achieve it. There is nothing different about you, the only person that can make you drink is YOU.

2. NOTHING TO GIVE UP

Keep it clear in your mind that there is nothing to give up. I can understand that stopping drinking seems difficult if you think that you are 'giving up' a genuine pleasure or crutch, but once you realise there is nothing to give up, it's easy. I don't mean that the disadvantages outweigh the advantages, I mean there are NO advantages. All the apparent advantages, were just that – apparent. The courage, confidence, relaxation, pleasure etc., were very simply illusions based on the removal of our natural fears. The advantages never actually existed. That is why you would feel just as stupid moping around for an alcoholic drink after you stop as you would do searching for Santa

Claus or fairies, because they DO NOT EXIST! I have illustrated time and time again in this book that alcohol will exist for a long time, but that all the things we were conditioned to believe that alcohol did for us, do not exist. That was all you were hooked on – the illusions. So remember there is nothing to 'give up', you are not making any sacrifice. It is the people who drink who make all the sacrifices.

3. NEVER SAY I C.A.N.T.

Constant **A**nd **N**ever-ending **T**orture. This is precisely what recovery is. Do you want to be in 'recovery' and just surviving from day to day or do you want to be fully recovered and living everyday? Never say "I *can't* have a drink" when you know fully that you can physically pick one up if you wanted to – there is nothing stopping you. You can inject yourself with HIV too, YOU JUST DO NOT WANT TO! You do not want to be a slave to alcohol any more, so do not torture yourself by telling yourself that you *can't*. Remove the **T** from the word and you have immediately removed the self imposed torture.

4. THINK DRINK

Do not try **not** to think about alcohol or worry if you are thinking about it a lot of the time. I have already explained why it is impossible to try not to think of something. Just make sure that whenever you are thinking about it, whether it is today, tomorrow, next week, or for the rest of your life – that you think *'I don't have to do that anymore, ISN'T IT GREAT, I'M FREE! I'M A NON-DRINKER!'* That way you can think about drinking every minute of the day and you will still be happy. It is *what* you think that makes the difference.

5. THERE IS NO SUCH THING AS AN ALCOHOLIC
(as society understands it)

You must get it clear in your mind there is no such thing as an alcoholic. Whether you thought you were one or not, your common sense should help you to realise that there is no such thing. You are just a normal person who fell for a very clever confidence trick, just like millions of others throughout the world. But unlike many others still stuck in this psychological trap, you are breaking free. Having made that decision to break free, NEVER begin to torture yourself by doubting it. The disease only exists for the people who *need* to drink, not for those who don't.

6. DO NOT FEEL DOWN – REJOICE IN YOUR FREEDOM!

There is nothing to feel down about. Start off with a happy frame of mind. The second you finish your final drink, it's over. Rejoice from the start, because you are free from the start. Do not turn into a whinging ex-drinker, there is nothing worse.

There is nothing to mope for and everything to feel happy about.

7. DO NOT COUNT DAYS

What is the point? What are you going to do, count the days since you stopped for the rest of your life? How pathetic would that be? Almost as pathetic, or sad, as the poor souls in A.A. who celebrate every year with a cake. The more candles you have on your cake the longer you have survived! You don't want to survive or hang on in there for the rest of your life, you want to live. So do it – live! Leave alcohol behind, it's something that you used to do. Now you don't have to.

8. DO NOT AVOID *ANY* SITUATIONS

You have stopped drinking, not living! Enjoy social gatherings from the start, they are so much more enjoyable when you are you!

9. NEVER SEE 'JUST THE ONE'

Drinking alcohol is drug addiction and a chain reaction. See the whole business of drinking for what it is, drug addiction on a tremendous scale. If you think there is genuine pleasure in one drink, you will think there is a genuine pleasure in a million. Face up to the fact that whether you like it or not, you have got a disease. It will not simply go away because you put your head in the sand. Like all crippling diseases, it not only lasts for life but gets worse and worse. The *easiest* time to cure it is NOW!

10. DO NOT USE ANY REPLACEMENTS

Avoid non-alcoholic beers or wines. These simply perpetuate the illusion that you have made a sacrifice.

11. DO NOT ENVY DRINKERS – FEEL SORRY FOR THEM.

Do not envy people who need to drink alcohol, there is genuinely nothing to envy. See drinkers as objects of pity, not envy. Most of them are not even aware that they are trapped. They have a progressive disease and feel dependent on a drug but most do not even know it. Is that something to envy? Once they realise that you are free and you are happy about stopping, they will envy *you*!

12. THIS IS NOT A SAFETY NET

Never think for one second that this method is a safety net. (This is further explained in the final chapter – "Final Warning").

Finally: follow all of these guidelines. They are your true and guaranteed *'twelve steps'* to freedom.

If you have understood all that I have said in this book, and realised how simple the alcohol trap is, and if you actually follow all of the instructions, then in no time at all you will receive the…

38
Biggest Buzz In The World

 The biggest buzz you will get from alcohol, is when you no longer *have* to take it. The feeling is one of elation and euphoria, a true mental and physical boost that is yours to recapture whenever you wish. This feeling will happen for you, if it hasn't happened already at some point during the adjustment period. I had the sense of joy and freedom even before I finished my final drink, but the biggest buzz was yet to come. During the first few weeks after I had stopped everything became so clear. It was at this stage that I realised that alcohol did absolutely nothing for me. I was going out, having fun and most of the time I wasn't even thinking about drinking. When I did think about it I became more and more elated each day. I knew that I never had to drink again. I could see this fairly clearly before I'd actually consumed my last drink, but during the first couple of weeks I frequently experienced (and still do today) 'the biggest buzz in the world' at not *having* to drink.

I must admit that I did suffer some physical pain when I stopped drinking – BRUISED LEGS when I kicked myself for not seeing it earlier. That, for me, was the most frustrating part. But it's like that damn rubix cube, it only appears difficult if you go about it the wrong way, once you have the solution everything gradually falls into place. The reason for my frustration was because it was like being locked in a prison for years then suddenly realising that I always had the key.

In the end I realised that I was my own jailer. I kept myself trapped by believing that there were genuine benefits in taking alcohol and that alcohol was somehow different from any other drug. Realise that you are your own jailer. There is only one person that can make it difficult for you to stop drinking and that is you. The key is in your mind, and this book is about showing **you** how to turn back time to how it was before you even started drinking.

The moment of euphoria, or 'the big buzz' will happen at some point during the first few weeks, if it hasn't already. This has nothing whatsoever to do with alcohol leaving your body, but simply the adjustment that I talked about. Do not sit around waiting for anything to happen, just get on with your life and enjoy purging the disease from your body and mind.

To be truthful it is very hard to describe just how wonderful it is to be free without coming across as evangelical! I am not an evangelist, I just want to show the world that what they have believed for so long about alcohol is wrong. It is just one big illusion. I want everyone who is hooked on alcohol to realise that they are. I want the world to see that alcohol *creates* insecurities but gives the illusion of courage. I want the drinking world to know that they are being conned.

If you are concerned that social gatherings, meals, birthdays, parties, holidays and lunches, will not be the same without alcohol, then you are correct, they are not the same;

THEY ARE INFINITELY BETTER!

I feel alive again, awake again, clear headed again. Do you remember what it was like to be a child at a party, that sense of excitement and fun. That is what I feel like now when I go out, I am just looking to be social, to dance and to have fun. When I felt dependent on alcohol the number one priority was to make sure I had a drink, everything else came second. *"I will talk to you in just a minute let me get a drink first!"*

My only question now is not why was it easy for me to stop drinking, but why did I ever think that it needed to be difficult? With an open mind and a few instructions, it's easy. Does this mean that all social gatherings are going to be brilliant from now on and there will be no low points? No. This book is about dealing with common sense and reality. Were all social gatherings fun while you were drinking? NO! Did you ever have bad days when you were drinking? Yes of course. I am not saying that you will never have a bad time from now on, what I <u>am</u> saying is that because you will be physically and mentally a lot stronger than you have been in years, any highs are that much higher and any lows that do come along are not going to seem as low as they were.

So, let yourself get excited, you are reclaiming your freedom and you are becoming free! When I first stopped drinking I used to hide the fact that I had stopped, such is the stigma at present about <u>not</u> drinking. I used to tell people that I was driving, or that I didn't feel like it at the moment or that I was taking medication so I couldn't. Now I want to tell the world. And so should you. There is no need to be embarrassed about the fact that you no longer have to drink. How have we reached a stage in our society where we have to justify <u>not</u> needing a drug?

Remember that the poor alcohol addicts are permanently having to justify their intake to themselves and everyone around them, you no longer have to justify anything......., so don't!

Every time I go out, I feel the buzz of *not* having to drink. I think what a relief I don't have to do that anymore. You will too, you won't be able to help yourself. Although one part of you will feel genuinely sorry for drinkers, another part will experience a sense of achievement, a sense of pride, a sense of being slightly different and rebellious, a sense of exhilaration and a sense of real and genuine FREEDOM.

Some people have described it as one of the best feelings they have ever had. Oh the joy you have to look forward to. Don't wait for it to happen, the minute you finish that final drink, you cut off the supply and you are;

ALREADY FREE AT THAT MOMENT!

Why wait to celebrate? If the whole object is to say *'isn't it wonderful, I don't need to drink anymore'* then why not say it from the start? John McCarthy didn't wait to celebrate and neither did Nelson Mandela, so why should you? When I passed my driving test, I didn't avoid telling anyone in case I couldn't drive next week! I knew that by next week I would be a **better** driver than I was when I first passed. That is why if anybody asks you why aren't you drinking, tell them the truth from the start,

BECAUSE I DON'T WANT TO ANYMORE or more importantly BECAUSE I DON'T *HAVE* TO ANYMORE!

If you do this then you can help me with my vocation in life which is to help every alcohol addict in the world see alcohol addiction for what it actually is so that we can finally....

39

End This Madness

On this tiny island alone, in the next fifteen to twenty minutes, (and every fifteen to twenty minutes), there will be two drink-driving convictions and two emergency medical admissions, one admission to a psychiatric hospital and one DEATH because of alcohol! They say that it's those who abuse alcohol who have these problems. But nobody ever abuses alcohol, alcohol always abuses its victim. Any form of drug addiction physically and mentally abuses its victim, it is never the other way around.

Alcohol kills over **ONE MILLION** people throughout the world every year. Nobody knows the true figure, as it is so hard to gauge. It destroys millions of lives in so many different ways on a daily basis. Our own government earns ten billion pounds annually from a disease which we know kills forty thousand of its own people every year and destroys the quality of lives for millions of others. We allow the industry to spend over TWO HUNDRED MILLION POUNDS advertising this drug every year in the UK. Alcohol is responsible for more suicides, more murders, more rapes, more beatings, more physical and verbal violence, more sexual abuse, more divorces, more financial ruin, and a general reduction of quality and length of life both for the addict and those around them, than ANY OTHER DRUG in the world! Our children's lives are being shaped by 'passive drinking' as we speak.

Alcohol drags society down in ways that have never truly been seen up until now. It is the largest confidence trick to fool mankind EVER, and it must be stopped!

You will now do your bit to help – just by being free. You are literally at the start of a massive shift in society's perception of alcohol. You are one of the elite, one of the few people that can now see alcohol for what it really is. We are only just beginning to change our perception and attitude towards the world's most used and accepted drug. You can help me to help others become aware of the trap that they are in, so that they too can be free and so that it is not just *accepted* that future generations will become dependent on a drug. It should not be the *'norm'* to drink alcohol, but the other way around.

Just by gaining your freedom, you will be helping to start moving attitudes towards alcohol in the same direction as those towards smoking. Smoking was also seen as 'cool', 'big', sociable, and an adult thing to do for many years. This perception of smoking is constantly changing. Over sixty percent of the population was smoking at one time, it is now thirty percent and dropping. Alcohol needs to go the same way – passive drinking destroys more lives than passive smoking ever will. Alcohol does nothing but destroy people mentally and physically. I am just a normal person who has found freedom, but I believe I am the most passionate person in the world about this subject and I will do everything in my power to help as many people as I can to break free from this slavery. My vocation is to cure the world of this disease.

What is the best way you can contribute? By simply being you – by going out as usual, by enjoying meals as usual, by doing all the things that you used to do. When other people see that it is possible to be free, when they see that you can easily enjoy life to the full without alcohol, when they see that you don't need alcohol any more, when they see you looking better and feeling better. When they see that you have more confidence, more courage, that you are more relaxed and that your life has improved in every single area, they will want to be part of it too. It's contagious!

Do not become a "holier than thou ex-drinker", there is really nothing worse. Always remember that you were once there yourself, so do not be too quick to judge. Remember that you used to *have* to drink too but you are now in a position where you are free and no longer have to. Anybody who is getting drunk around you is not choosing to drink, they *have* to drink. Just because they believe that they are choosing to drink does not change the reality of the situation.

This is why Prohibition did not work and could never work. You can not solve the alcohol problem by banning it or trying to pretend that it is not there. Once you have been deluded by alcohol, insecurities inevitably follow. The addict is then deluded into thinking that they cannot enjoy or cope with their lives without alcohol. The more it drags them down the more they feel the need for it. Choice does not come into it. This is why it is no good giving drinkers ultimatums like *"Either the drink goes or I go!"* The poor addict will pick the drink, not because they choose to, but because they have to. They feel as though coping without you would be less painful than coping without their crutch. If you ban alcohol, drinkers will want it even more, as it becomes the **CAN'T** syndrome on a massive scale. The forbidden *"gone off"* fruit!

All you need to know is that every drinker you meet, whatever the situation, will secretly envy you. They want to be in a position where they can enjoy themselves and cope with life without having to take a drug. They all wish they were free. They all want to be like you – a person who doesn't need to drink any more. Isn't that why you have read this book? Because you actually wanted to be a non-drinker, a normal person again? Remember that is what the drinker wants too. If he is drinking it is proof in itself that he wants to be free. The only reason why anybody drinks is to try and get to the position that the non-alcohol addict is already in.

The people who have finally realised that they are trapped would love to wake in the morning in the position that you will find yourself in no time at all, FREE from the whole slavery of being a drug addict. They will want it even more when they see just how happy you are to be free. Some will expect you to be getting uptight about not drinking. They will perhaps expect you to be moping or at least whinging a bit. But they will see that you are simply relieved and happy because you are free from drug addiction; free from an awful slavery which was slowly destroying you, physically and mentally. They will realise that you are not opting out of life, but going out and enjoying yourself just as before. They will think that you are incredible, unique, special, and super human. The most important part is that you will be feeling these things yourself.

The drinkers around you will want to be part of it. I am seeing a change around me all the time. People who before would never have even contemplated stopping drinking, are now either stopping or questioning their drinking like never before. Frequently, people around you may not openly say that they want to be free for fear that they *can't* do it, but the effect you will have on those people will literally be contagious. Everyone will soon want to know how you did it.

It may take time for society to make this shift in attitude, but it will happen. When it does you will know that you have helped in that process. You will help others to realise that people plainly and simply do not *need* alcohol. Then instead of <u>them</u> dragging <u>you</u> down, you will lift them up. However, you cannot force anybody to stop drinking, there are still members of my family who drink (they haven't read this book yet!) This is painful for me, as I can see they are in a sinking ship and missing out on the juice of life. Yet if I were to throw them a life jacket I know that they would simply toss it back to me. It is not that they are being difficult, it's because of the FEAR and INSECURITIES created by the drug that keeps them hooked. It takes a lot for people just to read this book or come to my clinic for a session. I admire you for overcoming your fears, reading the entire book and making the concrete decision to break free for the rest of your life.

You now realise that there is no reason why anybody should find it difficult to stop drinking. It is so easy when the brainwashing and illusions have been removed. But please remember that others may not understand yet. So if you were to turn into a "holier than thou" you would not be helping them, nor will it help if you pressure them. Simply be yourself and enjoy your freedom. They will soon pick up the book in no time at all. Then they will be in a position like you where they can finally take control of their own lives once more and experience a full and enjoyable…

40

L.I.F.E

Live In Fearless Excitement

Everything we need is within us already!

One of the biggest joys of being free is the sudden realisation that everything that we will ever need is within us already. The ability to meet challenge is built within us. The courage to overcome any fears that come along is built within us. We have the capability to feel joy and happiness at a moments notice. We have the finest drug in the world in its purest form already within us, and it's FREE of charge! It is LIFE FORCE. It is the buzz of being ALIVE, growing every day and meeting new challenges. Alcohol literally destroys your life force. It slowly makes you die inside. If you are not growing, you are dying there is no in between. Alcohol addicts have no idea just how much the drug is affecting their lives or how much it is ruling many aspects of their lives. They look around them and see that they are pretty much the same as everyone else. That is the problem, you don't <u>want</u> to be the same as over ninety percent of the population. Most people are missing out on the juice of life. Most people survive, but don't live. Most people have stress and not challenges. Most people are hooked!

Stress only becomes stress if you are not strong enough to handle it. An alcohol addict will always be more mentally and physically stressed than the person they would be if they didn't drink. Wouldn't it be lovely if there were a product which could:

Help us to relieve stress in an instant
Give us courage in an instant
Generate confidence in an instant
Make us happy and joyous in an instant
Relax us in an instant
Improve our social skills in an instant

Alcohol addicts are deluded into believing that alcohol can do all of those things and more. Not only does alcohol *not* achieve any of the above but it does the opposite.

The good news is that there is a product that *can* achieve *all* of the above in an instant, it is called the mind! How we think creates every emotion we have and all of us have the ability to tap into any emotion in an instant!

Children do not need alcohol if they get stressed and yet one of the most stressful periods in any human beings life is early childhood. Many children are unfortunately infected by passive drinking on a massive scale, so the natural tendency is for them to reach for a kind of escapism at some point. They are conditioned from birth to believe that alcohol can provide them with all their needs. The illusions created by the drug confirm this belief and their genuine courage and confidence is destroyed. It happens so slowly for most that they don't even realise. The sad thing is that they believe the opposite, they think that alcohol is giving them courage and confidence, but in fact they are slowly dying inside.

Without challenge or fear in your life you have no grounds on which to build or use courage. Without courage you can never grow, you can never learn and you can never build. Without fear you slowly wither away inside. Alcohol destroys courage. It removes natural fears and creates additional fears and insecurities that shouldn't even be there. It slowly kills people physically, but more importantly, it kills them emotionally, a little more EVERY DAY!

Our courage, our confidence, our happiness, our fulfilment, our joy, our lives are shaped by who we are right now as human beings. It doesn't matter how much money you have, if you stop growing as a person you will not be truly happy. Challenge or stress are wonderful tools to help you to shape and grow, and make you who you are.

You will now start to grow in ways beyond your current comprehension. Of course you will have challenges and stresses, but you will be much better equipped to take them on. Stress is an emotion like any other, without it you wouldn't grow.

I now love challenge. It is like a game that I cannot lose because the person I am can never be taken away. We are born with the best gifts of life. However gifts are pointless unless we use them. We are born with the gift of emotion. Happiness, love, joy and fulfillment are ours in a second if we want them. When you drink alcohol, you try to rely on alcohol to provide you with these emotions but it never does. Alcohol does the complete opposite.

The drug literally destroys your ability to LIVE. When you are a slave to any drug you accept a life of survival, instead one of growth, meaning and fulfillment. You will never be truly fulfilled while you are hooked on a drug. I have seen people who stop drinking but then go on to replace it with another drug. You do not need a replacement for drug addiction. You don't need a replacement for a disease that simply gets worse and worse and eventually becomes a living nightmare. If you feel that you need another drug to replace alcohol then you have missed the whole point. You genuinely do not need any drug. Everything we need for fulfillment, joy and happiness is right here, within us. We can have them whenever we wish, if we just tap into them.

Life is a hundred, or so, year holiday. Sometimes people believe that they got a lousy deal. They believe that their tour operator has gone bust, leaving them with a holiday from hell. What people sometimes fail to realise is that:

We are our own tour operators

This means that **we** can design the holiday of our dreams. Take charge of your life each and every day. Never forget about TODAY. We are all so busy working for tomorrow that we sometimes fail to appreciate today – this moment, this second of our lives. Many people play the "I'll be happy when..." game. I'll be happy when I earn this amount of money. I'll be happy when I get this new car. I'll be happy when I reach the top etc. Always living in the future thus missing today, right now. I still play the "I'll be happy when...." game, but I've changed the rules slightly. Now I'll be happy when...ever I want to be!

LIFE means LIFE. Now that you are breaking free you will always feel more alive, mentally and physically. This gives you the resources to tap into a quality of life you had forgotten even existed for you. Alcohol drags people down so much that they simply accept a secondary way of life. I had no idea just how much alcohol was affecting every area of my entire life because it happened so gradually, and I compared myself to other people. I can now compare myself to my old self. I now have more money, much better health, more peace of mind, more self respect, more courage, more confidence, so much more physical and mental energy that it's a joke, and I have my true freedom back again to always be me! And I love it!

Enjoy your freedom and never go back to drug addiction, no matter how long you have stopped for. The facts about alcohol *never* change. Enjoy the highs and learn from the lows.

To make sure that you have life long success here is ....

41

The Final Warning

THE BOOK IS NEVER THE SAME TWICE!
I just want to repeat that again as it is a very important part of the book...
THE BOOK IS NEVER THE SAME TWICE!!!

It is easy to stop drinking and to stay stopped providing that you understand that the book is never the same twice. I cannot repeat this point enough. I have said that if you follow *all* of the instructions then you will be free forever.

You need to understand this point more than any other – it's easy to stop drinking – but mental and physical torture to try and control. This is because alcohol is a drug and the nature of any drug is to take more and more. If you ever believe that you want to control it, then you have missed the point anyway. It means that you haven't fully understood the nature of the beast! Remember that you no longer want to exercise control anymore that is why you stopped.

The only danger with this method is that it makes it easy to quit. How can that be a danger I hear you ask. People that find it easy to stop can find it easy to start again. This is a category you do not want to find yourself in, as the book will not work a second time. This is because....in case I haven't mentioned it already,

THE BOOK IS NEVER THE SAME TWICE!

If you were ever *curious* to have a drink and thought to yourself *"well 'just the one' won't hurt"*. After all it was so easy to stop, that even if I did get hooked again, it wouldn't matter for I now have a route out. I will simply re-read the book! **NO NO NO NO NO NO NO NO NO NO NO NO NO NO NO NO NO NO NO NO NO!**

The information in this book is new to you at this moment. What I mean is that it has been presented in such a way that your brain would respond by saying: *"Ah, I have never seen it that way before that makes so much sense"*. This book is designed to inspire and excite you because of its sheer simplicity. If you were to get caught again and tried to re-read the book, the information and the way in which it is presented would no longer be new. You would find yourself skipping pages, saying *"yeah, I know that, I know that"*. You would then reach the end of the book and say *it* doesn't work anymore. THIS BOOK NEVER CHANGES, only the way in which the person reading it perceives the words.

Your perception would be different because your brain would *never* read it the same way again, no matter how hard you tried! But why would you ever want to read this book again? You would only ever need to pick up this book again if you were drinking alcohol again and why on earth would you ever want to do that?

This book is not a safety net, so do not use it as such. This is a key instruction. If you feel as though you need a safety net 'just in case', then again you have missed the point. Remember, just one drink *will* cost you over £100,000 and will keep you a slave for life. It will destroy you physically and mentally and affect the entire quality of your life forever. See it for what it is that way you cannot *crave* slavery, misery and the depletion of your mental and physical life, you can only jump for joy that you are free!

You picked up this book and have read it because you were either consciously or sub-consciously looking for an escape route from the alcohol trap. You have found one, so use it. Once you are free it would be ludicrous to ever go back again, especially when you know that it does *nothing* for you and that the chances of an easy and enjoyable escape the second time are virtually NIL!!

Alcohol addiction is an ingenious confidence trick and intelligent people do fall for ingenious confidence tricks, but what kind of person would ever fall for the same trick twice? Nobody, especially if they knew for certain that their life depended upon it.

The impact of this book would never be the same for you ever again if you were to have just 'one' drink. Keep the book by all means. It can be a tool if you need to reverse any brainwashing should it start to creep in. Never underestimate the power of brainwashing. Counter it if you ever feel it rearing its ugly head. But if you have just 'one drink' forget it – it's over!

There are few subjects that I am so adamant about. I have written this book because I want to see an end to the completely unnecessary suffering which alcohol causes to its victims and society in general. I am committed to helping the world get free FOREVER, not simply for a few weeks.

The world's perception of this drug will change, but it will take time to change such an ingrained belief. You will be part of that change. We are just at the beginning, but as your friend I urge you to always enjoy your freedom and to remember how lucky you are to be outside the cage. Keep it very clear in your mind that no matter how long you have stopped for, the grass is not greener on the other side. You already know that it isn't, that is why you are reading this book. So do not look back through rose coloured glasses. The facts about alcohol addiction **never** change, the drug will always be the same, no matter how long you have stopped for. It is a drug and that is why there is no such thing as 'one' drink for *anybody*, not just you. Why would you even want one? It does nothing for you. It was just an illusion. Whenever you remember occasions when you had a great time and you were drinking on those occasions, always bear in mind it wasn't because of the drink, it was in spite of it.

If you hit a moment of stress and somebody offers you a drink, you need to understand that you are already stressed enough at that point. The last thing you need is a life long addiction to go along with your stress! More importantly you will now know for certain that it would never solve the stress, in fact as with everything else, alcohol would do the complete opposite!

You *were* stuck in a mental prison. Now that you are free, you should not think that you have left anything behind. If you returned to look around the prison you would realise straight away that there was nothing there, but by then it would be too late. As you turned to leave the door would shut tight! The key to lifelong success is to imagine the prison with glass walls around it so that you can see that there is nothing there long before you even contemplate having 'one' drink. Looking inside the prison through glass walls is a great reminder of why you wanted to quit, why you wanted to escape. That way once again you will remind yourself of just how nice it is to be free.

There are so many advantages to being free that you will simply have to discover them for yourself. However, the biggest gain for you is this:

You started this book thinking that you were different to everybody else, you can finish this book knowing that you are!

How exciting is that?

People come to my sessions with doom and gloom written all over their faces. This is because society has set up the rules to say *they* are different to everybody else. Apparently these people should feel ashamed because they have fallen for the same confidence trick as over ninety percent of the population. The problem is that when they first enter my sessions they do feel ashamed. They feel at rock bottom before they come in. They feel as though they are in a no-win situation. What they don't understand, when they first arrive, is that they are way ***ahead*** of the game. They realise that they are trapped and that given the choice they would love to escape. I help to give them that genuine choice. Within no time at all it begins to dawn on them that they are in exactly the same position as everybody else – hooked on a drug; they leave knowing that they are not the same as everybody else, because they are no longer hooked.

Once this has been understood, it is one of the best feelings in the world.

Thank you for sharing your time with me and having the courage to finish this book and make the very easy jump to freedom. You are achieving something truly amazing. Every time I hear of someone breaking free, I get a feeling of tremendous satisfaction. I would love to hear from you. It would give me great pleasure to hear of your freedom and comments.

If for whatever reason we never get the chance to meet, I wish you a truly extraordinary life.

Best Wishes

Jason Vale

To contact us or for more information please phone 0845 1 30 28 29, email **info@thejuicemaster.com**, or visit my website **www.thejuicemaster.com**.